WELCOME
THE WORD
Celebrating the Liturgy
of the Word with Children

WORKSHEETS

WELCOME
THE WORD

Celebrating the Liturgy
of the Word with Children

WORKSHEETS

Joan Brown SND

GEOFFREY
CHAPMAN

Geoffrey Chapman
An imprint of Cassell Publishers Limited
Villiers House, 41/47 Strand, London WC2N 5JE, England
387 Park Avenue South, New York, NY 10016-8810, USA

First published 1992

British Library Cataloguing-in-Publication Data
A catalogue record for this title is available from
the British Library.

ISBN 0-225-66650-2

Printed and bound by Short Run Press Ltd, Exeter

These worksheets may be used in conjunction with
Welcome the Word by the same author (ISBN 0-225-66525-5),
also published by Geoffrey Chapman.

6 5 4 3 2 98 97 96 95 94

Contents

As these are worksheets, there are no page numbers on them. This listing indicates the sequence to help you find the worksheet for a particular Sunday.

INTRODUCTION

THE SEASON OF ADVENT
First Sunday of Advent, Years A, B, C
Second Sunday of Advent, Years A, B, C
Third Sunday of Advent, Years A, B, C
Fourth Sunday of Advent, Years A, B, C

THE SEASON OF CHRISTMAS
First Sunday after Christmas (Feast of the Holy Family), Years A, B, C
Second Sunday after Christmas, Years A, B, C
Feast of the Epiphany, Years A, B, C
Feast of the Baptism of the Lord, Years A, B, C

THE SEASON OF LENT
First Sunday of Lent, Year A
First Sunday of Lent, Year B
First Sunday of Lent, Year C
Second Sunday of Lent, Year A
Second Sunday of Lent, Year B
Second Sunday of Lent, Year C
Third Sunday of Lent, Year A
Third Sunday of Lent, Year B
Third Sunday of Lent, Year C
Fourth Sunday of Lent, Year A
Fourth Sunday of Lent, Year B
Fourth Sunday of Lent, Year C
Fifth Sunday of Lent, Year A
Fifth Sunday of Lent, Year B
Fifth Sunday of Lent, Year C

HOLY WEEK
Passion/Palm Sunday, Years A, B, C

Introduction

These worksheets are an additional resource for the Liturgy of the Word celebrated with children on Sundays.

They are a development of the themes of the three-year cycle as presented in *Welcome the Word*.

The aim of the worksheets is that the children, after celebrating the Liturgy of the Word on Sunday, will have a sheet to take home as a reminder of the Sunday Gospel message.

They will also help the children realise that what happens at Mass on Sunday is connected with the way they live during the week.

Included on the sheets are activities, prayers, motifs and texts taken from *Welcome the Word*, giving a summary each week of what the children have experienced at their Liturgy of the Word on Sunday.

BE ON THE WATCH

Today begins ADVENT

It is a time of waiting and preparing for the coming of Jesus. During Advent we prepare to celebrate Christmas, to remember Jesus' being born. And we also remember his promise to come again.

During Advent we remember God's wonderful gifts to us.

Jesus says, 'You will see signs, the golden sun and the silver moon and stars shining in the night sky. Let these remind you that I am coming. Be on the watch.'

In the stars draw some of God's gifts to you.

We remember especially the greatest gift of love that God gives us: JESUS.

Find the signs Jesus says remind us of his coming . . .

A M N N O O R S S S T U

Alleluia, alleluia! We long for your coming, Lord Jesus.

Alleluia!

PREPARE A WAY FOR THE LORD

Jesus wants to come into our lives. Do we make the way difficult for him, or easy?

How can we make the way in easy?

By smoothing the way with

P _ _ C _ SH _ R _ NG

K _ NDN _ SS TR _ TH

John the Baptist came with this message:

'Prepare a way for the Lord. Make your hearts ready to receive him. Make the path for him into your life easy.'

Many people who heard John decided to change their lives. They went to the River Jordan, where John baptised them.

What is the message John brings us from God?

How did the people who heard John prepare? What sign did they make?

What did this sign mean?

Write or draw here what you will do as a sign to prepare for Jesus coming.

How we make the road difficult:

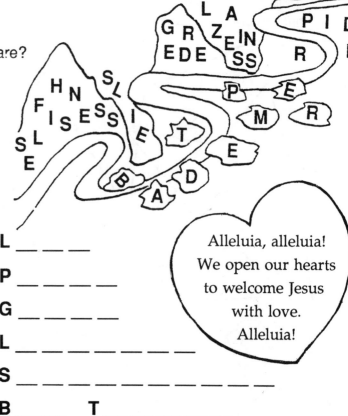

Alleluia, alleluia! We open our hearts to welcome Jesus with love. Alleluia!

L _ _ _ _

P _ _ _ _ _

G _ _ _ _ _

L _ _ _ _ _

S _ _ _ _ _ _ _ _ _

B _ _ T _ _ _ _ _ _ _

BE HAPPY!

JESUS IS COMING

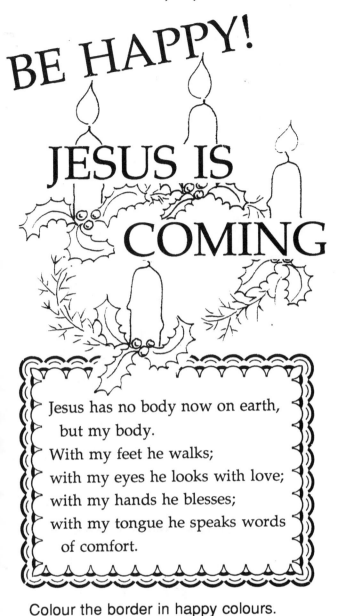

Jesus has no body now on earth,
  but my body.
With my feet he walks;
with my eyes he looks with love;
with my hands he blesses;
with my tongue he speaks words
  of comfort.

Colour the border in happy colours.

'Anyone who believes in me is happy.'

The King put John the Baptist in prison. But that did not stop John from hearing about the many wonderful things that Jesus was doing.

Match up the wonderful things Jesus did for people.

BLIND	**WALK**
DEAF	**LIVE**
LAME	**SEE**
SICK	**HEAR**
DEAD	**HEALED**

HAPPINESS CHAINS

Fill the chains with what you can do to spread HAPPINESS.

Alleluia, alleluia!
Let us be ready to welcome the Lord, for he comes.
Alleluia!

Make some more happiness chains for Christmas.

FILL US, LORD, WITH YOUR LOVE

'I am ready to do what God wants me to do.'

In each bell draw a picture or write the name of someone you love . . . people who love you.

'Rejoice, Mary,' the angel said. 'God has chosen you especially. You are going to have a baby boy. You must call him Jesus. He will be great. He will be called the Son of the Most High.'

JESUS' BIRTHDAY

DEC 25th

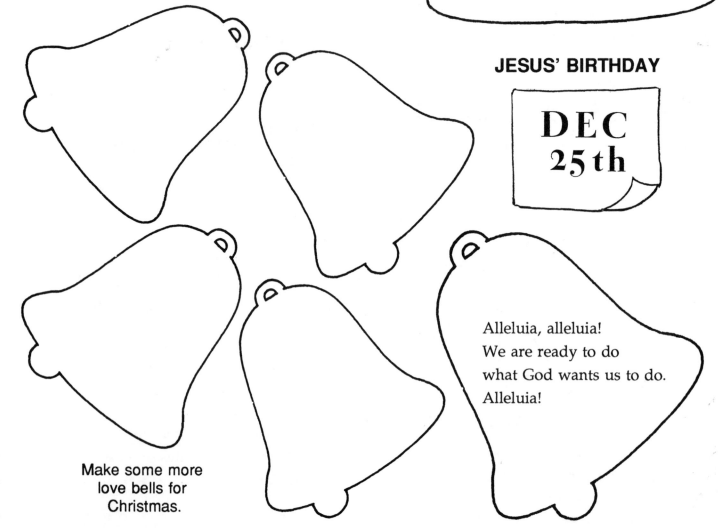

Alleluia, alleluia! We are ready to do what God wants us to do. Alleluia!

Make some more love bells for Christmas.

YEARS A, B, C FEAST OF THE HOLY FAMILY

They travelled home to Nazareth.

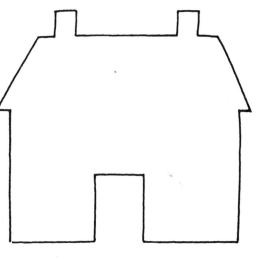

'I must be busy about my Father's work.' And Jesus grew in wisdom and in favour with God and all who knew him.

In this house write the names of your family.

In this house draw what is most important in your home.

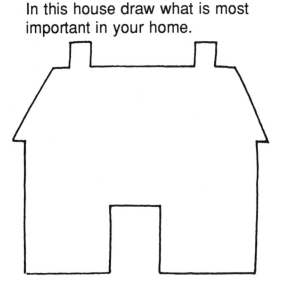

Draw yourself and your family having a happy day.

PRAYER OF GOD'S FAMILY

Our Father, who art in heaven,
Hallowed be thy name;
Thy kingdom come;
Thy will be done on earth as it is in heaven.
Give us this day our daily bread;
and forgive us our trespasses
as we forgive those who trespass against us;
and lead us not into temptation,
but deliver us from evil.

Alleluia, alleluia!
May Jesus and his Word
be at home with us.
Alleluia!

The light shone in the darkness
and could not be put out.

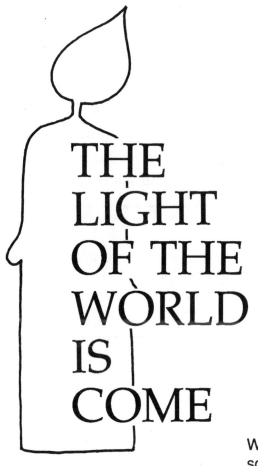

THE
LIGHT
OF THE
WORLD
IS
COME

All those who believe and
accept the Word and the light
are given great power,
the power to become children
of God.

The Christmas tree
is a sign of
Christmas happiness.

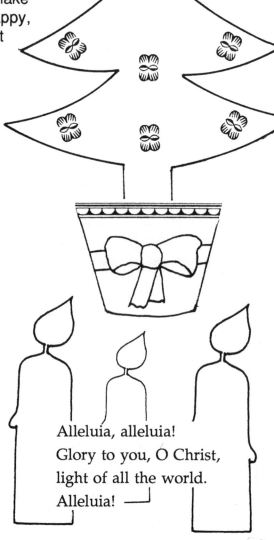

When you make
someone happy,
colour a light
on the tree.

1) Who is the LIGHT OF THE WORLD?

2) Another name for Jesus is

   W __ __ __ of G __ __ .

3) All who believe and accept the WORD and
LIGHT are given great power.

Power to become C __ __ __ __ __ __ __ __
of G __ __ .

When did you become a child of God?

What is your special name — the name
you were given at Baptism?
Write it here.

Alleluia, alleluia!
Glory to you, O Christ,
light of all the world.
Alleluia!

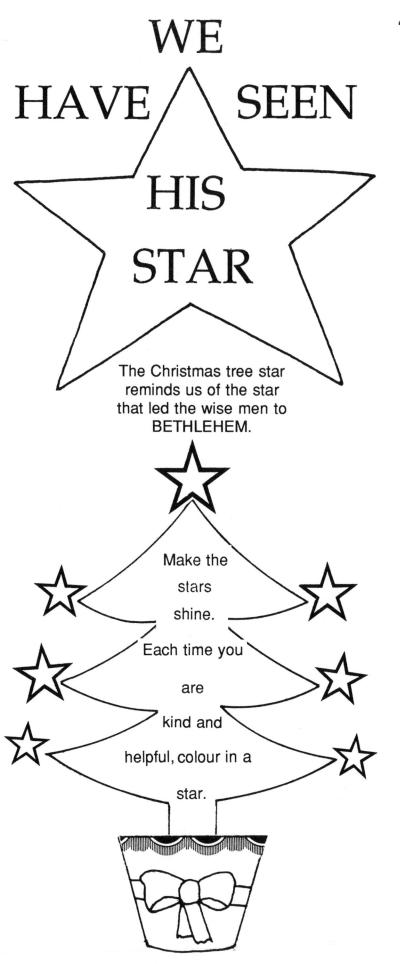

WE HAVE SEEN HIS STAR

The Christmas tree star reminds us of the star that led the wise men to BETHLEHEM.

Make the stars shine. Each time you are kind and helpful, colour in a star.

'We have seen his star and have come to worship him.'

The star led them to the place where Jesus was. They went in, and worshipped him. Then they offered him presents of gold, frankincense and myrrh.

Find the WISE MEN'S gifts.

Alleluia, alleluia!
We have seen his star
and have come to
worship him.
Alleluia!

WE ARE GOD'S BELOVED CHILDREN

Jesus came from Nazareth in Galilee to be baptised by John in the River Jordan.

No sooner had Jesus come up out of the water than he saw the heavens opening and the Spirit, like a dove, descending on him. And a voice came from heaven, 'This is my Son, the beloved.'

When were you baptised?

By whom?

What name were you given?

Who are your godparents?

What were you given at baptism?

What task were you given?

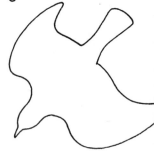

Colour the baptism candle. Write on the date of your baptism.

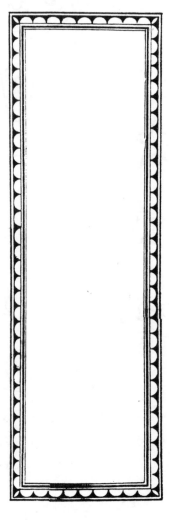

MY HOLY SPIRIT PRAYER ASKING FOR HELP TO BE LIKE JESUS

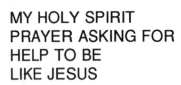

Alleluia, alleluia!
This is my Son, the beloved.
Listen to him.
Alleluia!

ANSWERS to last two questions
- a lighted candle
- to keep the light of faith burning brightly

GOD MADE ME IN HIS IMAGE

Jesus was led by the Spirit out into the wilderness.

'Worship God alone, and serve him.'

Fill in what the happy children are saying to God.

Give the children happy faces.

God hasn't just made us, he has made us to be like him, and to be happy with him. To do this, we follow Jesus in saying 'no' to anything that would harm us.

Praise to you, O Christ, our Saviour.
We do not live on bread alone
but on every word that comes
from the mouth of God.
Praise to you, O Christ, our Saviour.

BELIEVE GOD LOVES YOU

The Spirit led Jesus into the wilderness.

'Repent, and believe the Good News.'

The world is a beautiful place. Everything God has made is good. God does not make rubbish. God has made us more wonderful than anything else on earth. God loves us.

When Jesus left the desert he went to all the towns and villages sharing the GOOD NEWS.

In the cloud shapes fill in what you hear that makes you happy.

Colour the village. Add trees and flowers to make it beautiful. Put people there.

Praise to you, O Christ, our Saviour.
We do not live on bread alone
but on every word that comes
from the mouth of God.
Praise to you, O Christ, our Saviour.

JESUS GIVES US LIFE

Filled
with the Holy Spirit,
Jesus was led
into the wilderness.

He was in the
wilderness for forty days
and forty nights.

Fill in
how you
will share
your life
to make
other people
happy.

Colour the children.

Use your favourite
colours to bring the
flowers to life.

Praise to you, O Christ, our Saviour.
We do not live on bread alone
but on every word that comes
from the mouth of God.
Praise to you, O Christ, our Saviour.

LORD, IT IS GOOD TO BE HERE

Jesus took with him Peter, James and John, and led them up a high mountain to pray.

The world is full of signs of God's love. When you are good to be with, you are a sign of God's love.

And when they looked up, they saw no one — only Jesus.

Where do you most like to be?

Draw your favourite place.

In the clouds, draw when you are good to be with at home, at school, with friends.

Who do you most like to be with?

Draw your favourite person here.

Praise to you, O Christ, our Saviour.
This is my beloved son.
Listen to him.
Praise to you, O Christ, our Saviour.

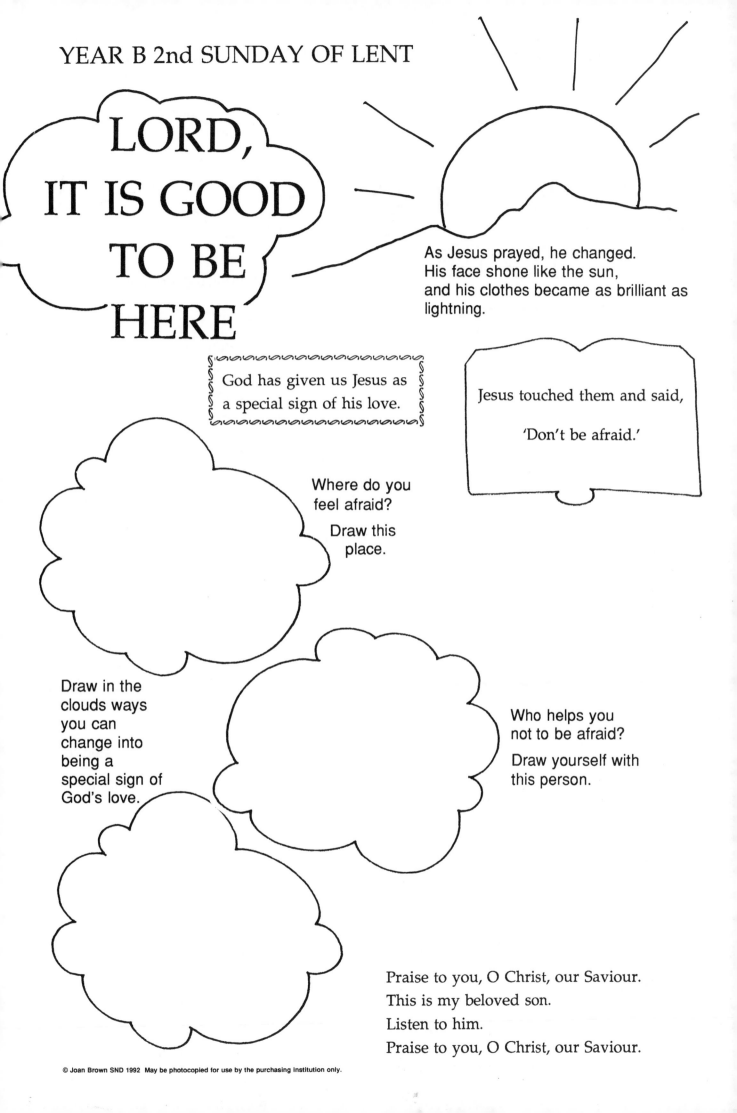

LORD,
IT IS GOOD
TO BE
HERE

As Jesus prayed, he changed.
His face shone like the sun,
and his clothes became as brilliant as
lightning.

God has given us Jesus as
a special sign of his love.

Jesus touched them and said,

'Don't be afraid.'

Where do you
feel afraid?
Draw this
place.

Draw in the
clouds ways
you can
change into
being a
special sign of
God's love.

Who helps you
not to be afraid?
Draw yourself with
this person.

Praise to you, O Christ, our Saviour.
This is my beloved son.
Listen to him.
Praise to you, O Christ, our Saviour.

LORD, IT IS GOOD TO BE HERE

'Lord, it's good that we are here.'

A bright cloud came and covered them with its shadow, and from the cloud came a voice which said:
     'This is my beloved Son.
          Listen to him.'

What sounds do you most like to hear? Draw what makes them.

In the clouds, draw when it is good to listen.

Who do you most like to listen to? When?

Draw this person.

Praise to you, O Christ, our Saviour.
This is my beloved son.
Listen to him.
Praise to you, O Christ, our Saviour.

Jesus said,
'Give me a drink.'

LIVING

WATER

I WILL

GIVE YOU

In the buckets,
draw the
help
you will give
to people
this week.

'Anyone who drinks the water
that I shall give will never
be thirsty again.'

Write in the shell
the date
when you
became a
child of God
by water
and the
Holy Spirit.

Praise to you, O Christ, our Saviour.
Lord, give us living water.
Praise to you, O Christ, our Saviour.

WE ARE GOD'S TEMPLES

In the birds and sheep, write or draw what you can give to God.

Jesus said, 'You have made my Father's house into a market!'

In the children, fill in all the nice things about yourself and a friend.

Praise to you, O Christ, our Saviour.
God loved the world so much
that he gave us his only Son.
Praise to you, O Christ, our Saviour.

ANOTHER CHANCE

'Look, this is the third year in a row that there has been no fruit on this tree. Cut it down, and plant something else that will give us fruit.'

'Sir,' the gardener replied, 'let's try just one more year.'

Fill the trees with the names of people who, with God's love and care, can become his friends.

God our Father,
you made us and you love us.
You know us by name.
You want us to produce good
fruit in our lives.
Give us strength to produce
the fruit you want.
We pray too for all the people
who have already been fruitful.

Praise to you, O Christ, our Saviour.
Change your ways, says the Lord,
for the kingdom is near.
Praise to you, O Christ, our Saviour.

The man went, washed, and he could see.

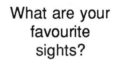

Jesus asked the man,
'Do you believe in the Son of Man?'
'Who is he?' the man replied.
'You are looking at him', Jesus said.

What are your
favourite
sights?

In the
eyes,
write or draw
what you
see that
makes you
happy.
At home . . .
At school . . .
With friends . . .
and . . .
and . . .

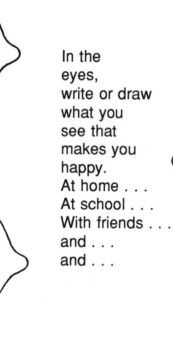

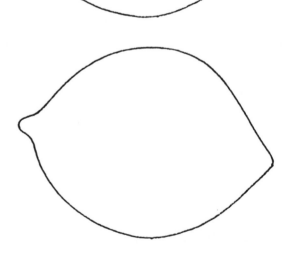

Praise to you, O Christ, our Saviour.
Lord, grant that we may see.
Praise to you, O Christ, our Saviour.

OUR LIGHT

'Those who live by the truth live in the light.'

Jesus says,

'I am the light of the world.'

JESUS

This is your Baptism candle. Write your name on it.

In baptism you,_____, were given a lighted candle. You were asked to keep the LIGHT of CHRIST burning brightly in your life.

Use your favourite colours to decorate this candle.

'I promise to keep the light of Christ burning brightly in my life.'

Write one word in each candle that shows you follow Jesus.

Praise to you, O Christ, our Saviour.
Lord, fill our hearts
with the light of your Gospel.
Praise to you, O Christ, our Saviour.

YEAR C 4th SUNDAY OF LENT

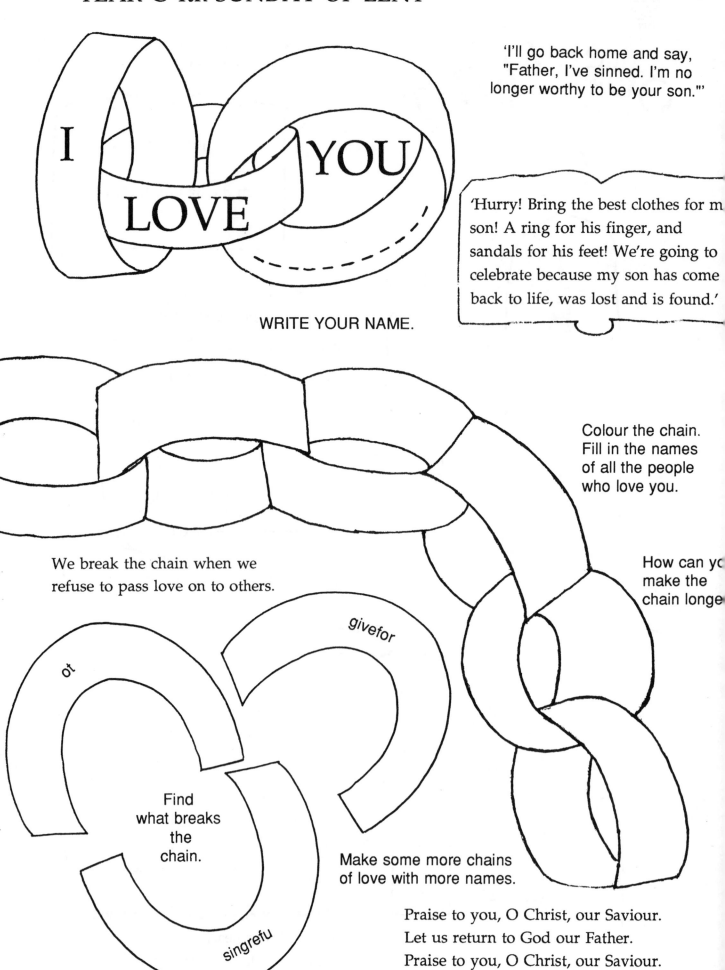

I LOVE YOU

'I'll go back home and say, "Father, I've sinned. I'm no longer worthy to be your son."'

'Hurry! Bring the best clothes for m son! A ring for his finger, and sandals for his feet! We're going to celebrate because my son has come back to life, was lost and is found.'

WRITE YOUR NAME.

Colour the chain. Fill in the names of all the people who love you.

We break the chain when we refuse to pass love on to others.

How can yo make the chain longe

givefor

ot

Find what breaks the chain.

Make some more chains of love with more names.

singrefu

Praise to you, O Christ, our Saviour.
Let us return to God our Father.
Praise to you, O Christ, our Saviour.

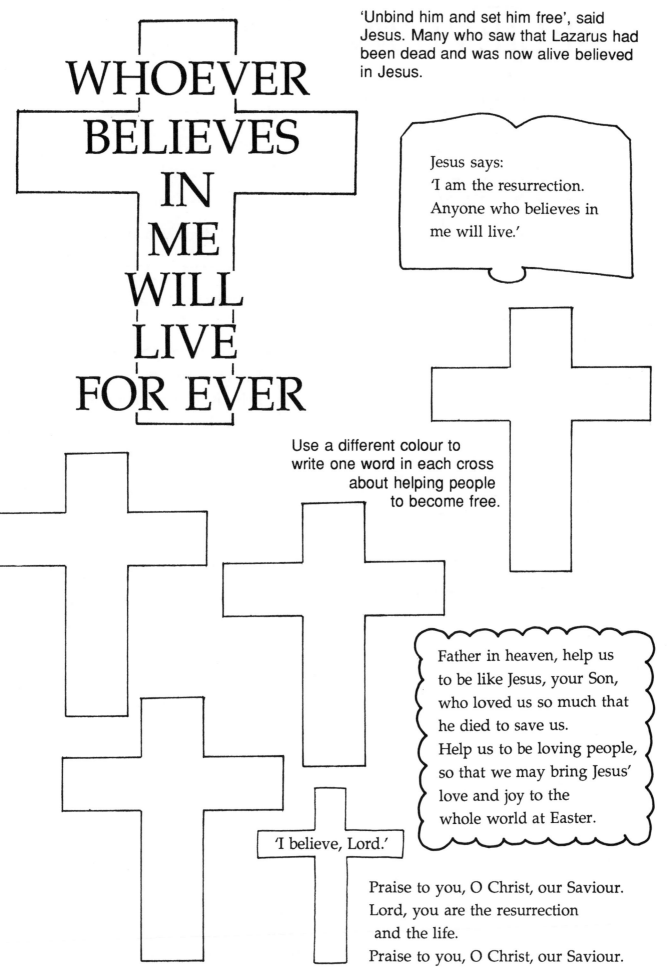

WHOEVER BELIEVES IN ME WILL LIVE FOR EVER

'Unbind him and set him free', said Jesus. Many who saw that Lazarus had been dead and was now alive believed in Jesus.

Jesus says:
'I am the resurrection. Anyone who believes in me will live.'

Use a different colour to write one word in each cross about helping people to become free.

Father in heaven, help us to be like Jesus, your Son, who loved us so much that he died to save us.
Help us to be loving people, so that we may bring Jesus' love and joy to the whole world at Easter.

'I believe, Lord.'

Praise to you, O Christ, our Saviour.
Lord, you are the resurrection and the life.
Praise to you, O Christ, our Saviour.

BELIEVE IN ME AND LIVE FOR EVER

'The time has come for me to be glorified.'

Jesus says,
'My father will glorify me
and when I am lifted up
I shall draw you all to myself.'

In each cross name a way to grow more like Jesus.

We have the power to grow into beautiful people.

Father in heaven,
help us to grow more like Jesus every day.
He died to give us new life.
Help us to die to selfishness and misery,
and to be alive to love and happiness this Easter.

In between the crosses, draw some of these ways.

Praise to you, O Christ, our Saviour.
Anyone who wants to serve the Lord must follow him.
Praise to you, O Christ, our Saviour.

YEAR C 5th SUNDAY OF LENT

I ❤ **I LOVE YOU**
- - - - - - - - -

Write your name.

'Let the person who has not sinned be the first one to throw a stone.'

'Go on your way, and do not sin any more.'

In this heart, fill in what you like most about your friend.

In this heart, fill in what you like most about yourself.

Draw your friend here.

Draw yourself here.

Heavenly Father,
we are each filled with the treasure of your gifts to us.
Help us to love and care for each other, to value your treasure in ourselves and others.

Praise to you, O Christ, our Saviour.
Come back to me with all your heart, says the Lord.
Praise to you, O Christ, our Saviour.

THE STORY OF JESUS' WALK OF LOVE

Help Jesus on his walk of love by drawing the pictures.

1.
Pilate is asking,
'What shall I do with Jesus?'

2.
Roman soldiers are making a crown
of thorns. They put it on Jesus.
They dress him in a purple cloak.

3.
Jesus is carrying his cross to Calvary.

4.
Simon helps Jesus to carry the cross.

5.
The women are crying.

6.
The soldiers have stripped off Jesus' clothes.

7.
Jesus is nailed on the cross.

8.
With a loud cry, Jesus dies.

9.
They put Jesus in the tomb.
They roll a large stone across the
entrance of the tomb, and go away.

Praise to you, O Christ, our Savior

Jesus gave himself for us,

even accepting death.

Praise to you, O Christ, our Savior

ALLELUIA! ALLELUIA!

JESUS IS RISEN!

'Mary!' And at once Mary knew that this was Jesus.

Jesus told her to go and tell the other disciples that she had seen him, and all the things he had said to her.

Jesus asked Mary to give a message to his friends.

Use your favourite colours to colour this Easter card.
What Easter message can you put on it for your friends?

Easter is the greatest, the most important celebration of the friends of Jesus, because we celebrate that Jesus, who died, is alive and can never die again.

Alleluia, alleluia!
Christ is risen.
Let us celebrate!
Alleluia!

'Thomas, here are my hands; come, put your fingers in the holes. See my side; come, put your hand in. Doubt no longer, but believe.'
Thomas said, 'My Lord and my God.'

Jesus said, 'You believe because you can see me. Happy are those who have not yet seen and yet believe.'

The cross is a glorious cross. It is where Jesus conquered death, to rise to give us new life. The cross is the sign of Jesus' victory.

God our Father,
full of life and goodness,
full of love and beauty.
You share everything with us,
even your only Son, Jesus.
Father, we thank and praise you
for the new life
which Jesus gives us
by his death and resurrection.

Draw here what makes you happy.

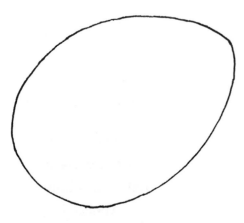

Fill the eggs with what you believe about Jesus. Then colour them with your favourite colours.

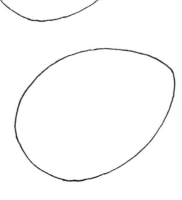

Alleluia, alleluia!
Happy are those
who believe in Jesus.
Alleluia!

WE HAVE SEEN HIM

'Didn't our hearts burn within us as he talked to us on the road?' they said to each other. They went straight back to Jerusalem to tell the others.

When they sat at the table, Jesus took the bread, blessed it, broke it, and shared it with them. Immediately they recognised that it was Jesus, but he vanished from their sight.

In the hearts, write or draw what helps you to remember Jesus at home, at school, with friends, and with your family.

Alleluia, alleluia! Happy are you when you meet Jesus on the road. Alleluia!

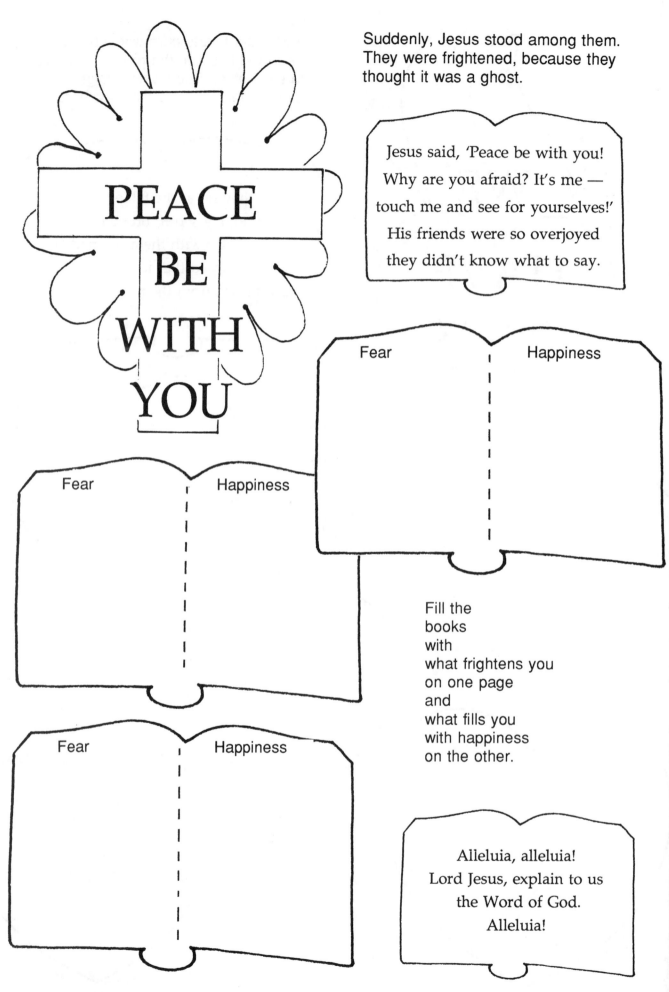

Suddenly, Jesus stood among them. They were frightened, because they thought it was a ghost.

PEACE BE WITH YOU

Jesus said, 'Peace be with you! Why are you afraid? It's me — touch me and see for yourselves!' His friends were so overjoyed they didn't know what to say.

Fear   Happiness

Fear   Happiness

Fill the books with what frightens you on one page and what fills you with happiness on the other.

Fear   Happiness

Alleluia, alleluia!
Lord Jesus, explain to us
the Word of God.
Alleluia!

IT IS THE LORD!

They heard a man calling to them from the shore.

As they got near the shore

John recognised the man

on the shore and said,

'It's Jesus!'

On the boat draw the people you are happy to see . . . or write their names.

In each fish,
draw how someone
makes you
happy.

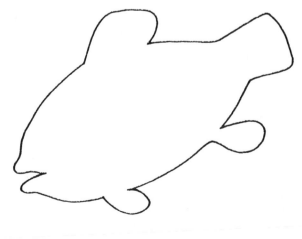

Alleluia, alleluia!
Jesus, you are the Lord.
Alleluia!

JESUS LOVES
HIS
SHEEP

Jesus says,
'I am the good shepherd.
I know my sheep and they know me.'

'I love my sheep,

and I will protect them

with my life.'

Write the
names of your
family and friends
in the sheep and
what Jesus loves
about each one.

Lord Jesus, our loving shepherd,
help us to hear you always
and to say 'yes'
when you call our names.

Write your name
in this sheep,
and what Jesus
loves about you.

Alleluia, alleluia!
'I am the good shepherd,'
says Jesus.
'I know my sheep and
they know me.'
Alleluia!

YEAR A 5th SUNDAY OF EASTER

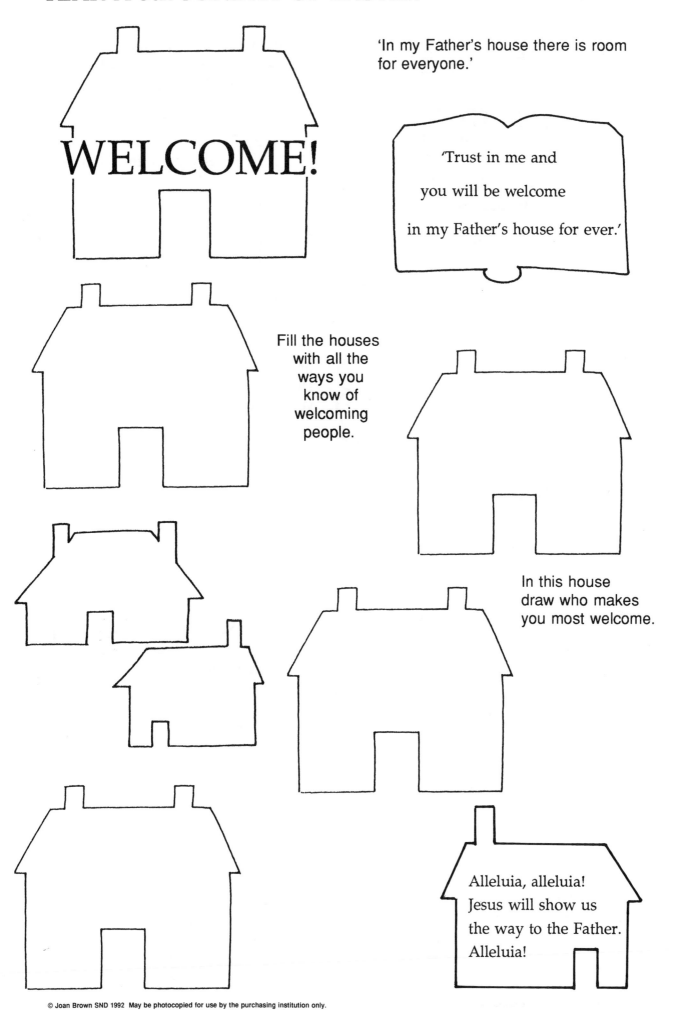

WELCOME!

'In my Father's house there is room for everyone.'

'Trust in me and you will be welcome in my Father's house for ever.'

Fill the houses with all the ways you know of welcoming people.

In this house draw who makes you most welcome.

Alleluia, alleluia! Jesus will show us the way to the Father. Alleluia!

JESUS
IS THE
VINE

On the vine there are many branches.
Some are full of beautiful fruit
but some have none.

Jesus says, 'I am the true vine,

so remain in me and you will

bear much fruit to the glory

of my Father.'

Write your name
on the grapes.
Draw the best thing
you have ever done.

In the grapes, draw some
other things you are good at.

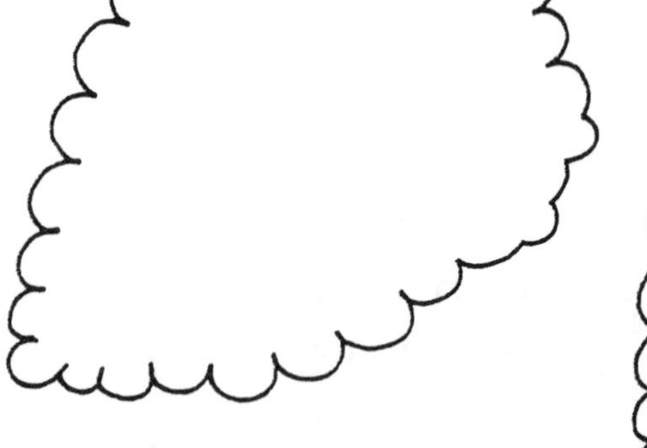

Alleluia, alleluia!

Those who bear fruit

give glory to the Father.

Alleluia!

I
LOVE
YOU

YOUR
NAME

Jesus says,
'My children,
I have something special to ask that
you do above all else.
I want you to love one another
as I love you.'

'By the love that you have for
one another everyone will
know that you are my friends.'

Colour the hearts.
Write or draw
in them
all the
people you
love.

Write
in this heart
who loves you most.

Alleluia, alleluia!
This is my command,
that you love one another
as I love you.
Alleluia!

A GIFT FROM JESUS

'Love one another as I have loved you.'

In the box put the gift you would like most.

'I will ask my Father to send you the Holy Spirit to be your friend for ever.'

In the gift tags, write the names of your family and friends. Draw the gift you would most like to give each one.

Alleluia, alleluia!
Anyone who loves God
listens to his Word.
Alleluia!

GLORY BE TO THE FATHER

'I pray for all those in the world who will believe in me now and forever.'

'I pray that they will all be one family, just as you and I are. I have shared my glory with them.'

Fill the hands with the names of the friends you pray for.

What do you pray for, for them? What do you share with them?

Draw some more prayer hands with more names.

Alleluia, alleluia!
I will not leave you, says the Lord,
I will come to be with you.
Alleluia!

COME HOLY SPIRIT

'We hear them preaching in our own language about the marvels of God.'

They were all filled with the Holy Spirit and began to preach the Good News.

Write or draw in the flames some of the wonderful things done to help people.

ALLELUIA

ALLELUIA

ALLELUIA

Come, Holy Spirit, fill our hearts with the fire of your love.

JESUS IS THE CHOSEN ONE OF GOD

'Here is Jesus,
the Chosen One of God.'

'Yes, I have seen and I
believe that Jesus is the
Chosen One of God.'

Fill the dove
shapes with
what you see
that helps you
to believe in
Jesus.

Alleluia, alleluia!
Here is the Lamb of God
who takes away
the sin of the world.
Alleluia, alleluia!

FOLLOW ME

. . . .TELL OUT THE GOOD NEWS

'The Kingdom of God is near, turn to God.'

Jesus went round all Galilee, teaching the people, telling out the Good News, and curing all kinds of sick people.

Fill the shells with Good News for

a lame person

a deaf person

a blind person

Fill the fish with what is Good News for you.

Alleluia, alleluia! Jesus told out the Good News of the Kingdom, and cured many people. Alleluia!

YEAR A 4th SUNDAY IN ORDINARY TIME

When Jesus saw the crowds, he climbed a little hill, where he sat down. His friends joined him, and he began to tell the people how to be happy.

HOW TO BE HAPPY

Jesus says:

'Happiness is wanting

God in your life.'

On the children's cards, fill in what makes you happy.

Alleluia, alleluia!
Father, let your face
shine on us.
Keep us in your love.
Alleluia!

YEAR A 5th SUNDAY IN ORDINARY TIME

SHINE LIKE A LIGHT

'Let your light shine,
do not hide it under a bucket.
Then everyone will know what God means to you,
and they will give him praise.'

Jesus says:

'You are the light of

the world.'

Fill the lights with what gives praise to God and makes them shine.

How do you praise God?
Write a PRAISE WORD in the candle.

What does not praise God?
Fill the bucket with what hides the Light.

Alleluia, alleluia!

Jesus is the Light

of the world.

All who follow him

have the light

of life.

Alleluia!

'Do good to everyone you meet.'

Jesus says to his friends:

'I love you all very much.

I want you to be happy.'

LOVE
IS
HIS WAY

Fill the
stars with the
names of your friends
and what
makes
them
happy.

Write or draw here how
friends make you
happy.

Alleluia, alleluia!

Speak, Lord, we are listening.

Your Word will bring us life.

Alleluia!

YEAR A 7th SUNDAY IN ORDINARY TIME

LISTEN!

'Listen!' said Jesus. 'Listen really hard!'

'Treat everyone with love and kindness, just as you would like them to treat you.'

Fill the hearts with what you like to hear.

Thank you, heavenly Father,
for the song of the birds;
for the sound of the sea;
for the homely sounds of baby crying;
and mummy calling me in for tea;
for daddy's laugh and the sound of his feet
when he comes home at night.
Thank you, Father, for the sounds in the night,
when I'm all tucked up tight.

Write here the names of people who are kind to you.

Alleluia, alleluia!

Lord, give us listening hearts.

Alleluia!

WE ARE PRECIOUS

Look all around you at the flowers. Look at the birds in the sky. If God cares so much for these, he cares much, much more for you who are so precious to him.

Jesus says:

'Do not worry about

anything.'

TO GOD

Fill the children and the birds with how you are precious to God.

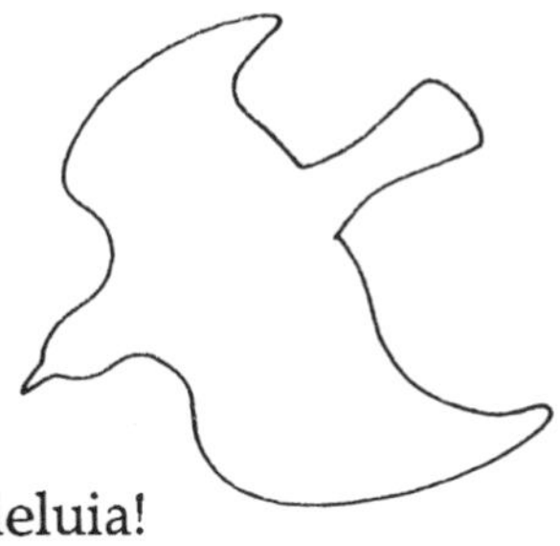

Alleluia, alleluia!
Your word is truth, O Lord.
Keep us true to you.
Alleluia!

BUILD

ON

LOVE

'Listen to me and try to do as I say, and you will be like the wise man who built his house on rock.'

Jesus says:

'If you love God,

you must show this

love in your lives.'

Jesus says that just as the house is safe when it is built on rock, so we are safe on the rock of God's love.

Write the names of the people who love you.

Fill the houses with how you show love at home.

Alleluia, alleluia!
If you love me, keep my word.
Then my Father will come
and make his home with you.
Alleluia!

FOLLOW JESUS

'Matthew', Jesus called, 'follow me.'

'I have not come

to call those who are good,

but to call sinners.'

Write the names of people who follow Jesus.

_____

_____

_____

_____

Fill the banners with different ways to follow Jesus.

Alleluia, alleluia!

Father, open our hearts

to hear the call of Jesus.

Alleluia!

SERVE THE LORD

Jesus felt sorry for the great crowd of people that had come to listen to him because there was no one to help them.

WITH GLADNESS

So Jesus called his friends together, and gave them the power they needed to help the people.

In the children, draw the friends who help you. Write their names.

Write the names of people who you help here.

_____

_____

_____

_____

Alleluia, alleluia!
My friends listen to my voice, says Jesus.
I know them and they know me.
Alleluia!

DO NOT BE AFRAID

'You can buy sixteen sparrows for a penny, but if one falls to the ground and dies, God, your loving Father, knows all about it.'

Jesus says: 'You need never be afraid of anything. You are worth more than hundreds of sparrows.'

Fill the sparrows with all the good things about yourself.

Alleluia, alleluia! Jesus gives us the power to be his friends. Alleluia!

WELCOME, JESUS!

'Even if it is only a cup of cold water that you give to my friends, you will be rewarded.'

Jesus says: 'Anyone who makes my friends welcome is welcoming me.'

When we welcome a friend of Jesus, we welcome Jesus.

Fill the cups with ways of making friends welcome.

Fill this cup with who makes you welcome.

Alleluia, alleluia!

Open our hearts, Lord, to welcome your friends.

Alleluia!

COME TO

ME

'I praise and bless you, Father,
Lord of heaven and earth,
for hiding your secrets from the
wise and learned,
and sharing them with children.'

Jesus says, 'My yoke
is easy and my burden
is light.'

Fill the yokes
with what you
find easy
to do
for Jesus.

Lord, you are faithful
in all that you say,
and loving in all that you do.

Support all who fall,
comfort the burdened,
and help all
who come to you for help.

Alleluia, alleluia!
Bless you, Father,
for showing the truth to children.
Alleluia!

LISTEN!

Jesus says: 'Imagine that you are a farmer going out to sow your seeds.'

'Some seeds fall on good ground with rich soil, where they will grow up strong and produce a good crop.'

Fill the flower shapes with ways you would like to grow up.

This is the seed of (write your name).

Alleluia, alleluia!
Speak, Lord,
your servants are listening.
Alleluia!

THE
KINGDOM
OF HEAVEN
IS LIKE . . .

The good seed
begins to grow
beautifully.

Jesus says,
'We'll put the
good crop in
the barn.'

Fill the seeds with
how you are growing
in goodness and love.

Alleluia, alleluia!
Help us, Lord,
to grow in goodness and love.
Alleluia!

SEEK THE KINGDOM OF HEAVEN

Jesus says: 'The Kingdom of heaven is like a treasure.'

Fill the chests with what you treasure that makes you happy.

'Nothing would make the merchant happy until it was his.'

Alleluia, alleluia!
I call you friends
because I have shared all my
Father's secrets with you.
Alleluia!

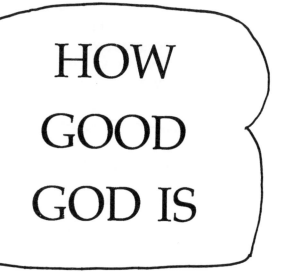

HOW GOOD GOD IS

'But we have only five loaves and two fishes! That's not enough to share!'

Jesus took the bread and fish, blessed them, broke the bread, and gave it to his friends. They shared it with the people, and everyone had plenty to eat.

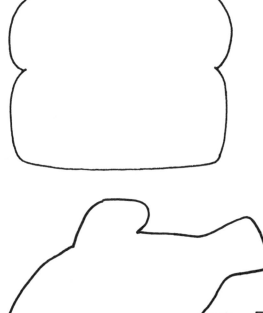

Fill the shapes with what your family and friends share with you.

Alleluia, alleluia!
Anyone who comes to me
will never be hungry.
Alleluia!

YEAR A 19th SUNDAY IN ORDINARY TIME

TRULY, YOU ARE THE SON OF GOD

Suddenly, when they were far out, a storm blew up. The little boat was tossed up and down in the giant waves. It was dark and Jesus' friends were very afraid.

Jesus says:

'It is I.

Do not be afraid.'

Fill the boats with the times your family and friends help you.

Alleluia, alleluia! Truly, you are the Son of God.

Alleluia!

LET ALL PEOPLES PRAISE YOU, GOD

The woman came up to Jesus, knelt at his feet and begged, 'Lord, help me!'

'Woman', said Jesus, 'you have great faith. Your prayer will be answered.'

Dress the children in different national costumes of the world.

Let all peoples praise you, God, let all peoples praise you.

Let the nations be glad and rejoice. For you rule the world with justice. You rule all peoples with fairness, you guide the nations on earth.

O God, be gracious and bless us, may your face shed its light upon us. May your ways be known on earth. May all nations know your saving help.

Alleluia, alleluia! Lord, increase our faith. Alleluia!

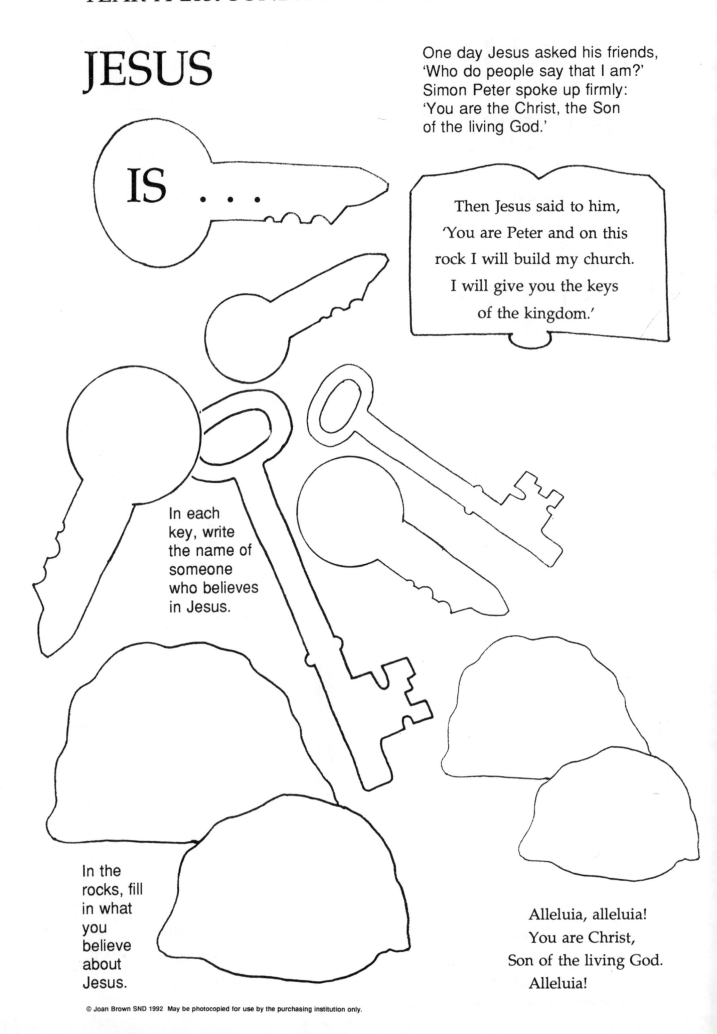

JESUS

IS . . .

One day Jesus asked his friends,
'Who do people say that I am?'
Simon Peter spoke up firmly:
'You are the Christ, the Son
of the living God.'

Then Jesus said to him,
'You are Peter and on this
rock I will build my church.
I will give you the keys
of the kingdom.'

In each
key, write
the name of
someone
who believes
in Jesus.

In the
rocks, fill
in what
you
believe
about
Jesus.

Alleluia, alleluia!
You are Christ,
Son of the living God.
Alleluia!

IS ANYTHING WORTH MORE THAN LIFE?

'Is there anything worth more than your life?'

Jesus said, 'Anyone who wants to be one of my followers must take their cross and follow me.'

Loving Father,
fill our hearts with your love
and with the desire to please you
in all that we do with our lives.
Help us to know you more each day,
to love you more dearly,
to follow you more closely.
Help us when times are difficult
and the way is hard.
Let us have no fear
as we follow in your footsteps.

Fill the crosses with what is precious about your life.

Alleluia, alleluia!
Take up your cross
and follow me.
Alleluia!

I WILL

BE

WITH YOU

Jesus says to his friends:
'I have something very important
to say to you.'

'Wherever two or three

meet in my name, I shall

be there with them.'

Draw yourself and your friends
having a happy time together.

Alleluia, alleluia!
Let us love one another
as Jesus loves us.
Alleluia!

FORGIVE FROM YOUR HEART

Peter asked Jesus, 'Suppose someone does me wrong, how often must I forgive them?'

'The king had pity, cancelled the whole debt, and let the man go free.'

Fill the hearts with ways you are loved and forgiven.

Alleluia, alleluia!
Forgive us
as we forgive others.
Alleluia!

YEAR A 25th SUNDAY IN ORDINARY TIME

GOD IS LOVE

Draw the most generous person you know or write their name.

Jesus told this story:
'The Kingdom of heaven is like a farmer who went out very early in the morning to employ people to work in his vineyard.

'Those who had worked all day began to grumble. "It's not fair! We worked all day, and got only as much as those who worked for just an hour!"'

'The farmer reminded them they had agreed to work for one pound when he hired them. "Why grumble", he said, "because I choose to be generous?"'

In the other coin shapes, draw some of the ways people are generous to you . . . at home . . . at school . . . at play . . .

Alleluia, alleluia!
Lord, you are just and loving, and your goodness lasts for ever.
Alleluia!

TAKE MY HANDS

'My son, I want you to go and work in my vineyard today.' The boy answered, 'No, I won't!' And off he went. But later in the day, he thought better of it, and went along to the vineyard to do the work his father had asked.

'My son, I want you to go and work in my vineyard today.' The second son replied, 'Certainly, Father.' But he didn't go.

Then Jesus said to his friends, 'Which of these two sons did what his father wanted?'

Fill the hands with generous things to do.

Lord Jesus, your love for us is so great that you did not refuse to give up your whole life for us. Help us to be generous so that we grow more like you each day. Amen.

Alleluia, alleluia! To love God is to hear his word and to do his will. Alleluia!

LORD,

FILL

US

WITH

YOUR LOVE

Jesus told his friends this story: 'There once was a rich man who owned a great deal of land. One day he decided to plant a vineyard.'

'I'll send my only son', he said, 'because they will respect him.'

Fill the grapes with what you think are the most beautiful, most wonderful parts of Creation.

You can write, draw or stick in pictures.

Alleluia, alleluia!
Lord, we belong to you.
Everything we have is yours.
Alleluia!

THE HONOUR OF YOUR PRESENCE

name _ _ _ _ _ _ _ _

IS REQUESTED IN THE KINGDOM

Jesus says, 'The Kingdom of heaven is like a king who prepared a wonderful party for his son's wedding.'

'Go out to the streets and invite anyone you meet to come to the wedding.'

Fill the invitation cards with celebrations you have enjoyed.

Alleluia, alleluia!
Lord, you have prepared
a banquet for us.
Alleluia!

GIVE TO GOD WHAT IS HIS

'Please tell us, is it right that we who are Jews should have to pay taxes to Caesar, the Roman ruler?'

'Very well then', said Jesus, 'give back to Caesar what is Caesar's, and give to God what belongs to God.'

Each of us is different; each of us is special. We have each been given special gifts by God, and all that he wants in return is that we use those gifts to give him glory and praise.

Fill the coins with God's special gifts to you.

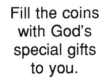

Alleluia, alleluia! Praise to God our Father for the many gifts he gives us. Alleluia!

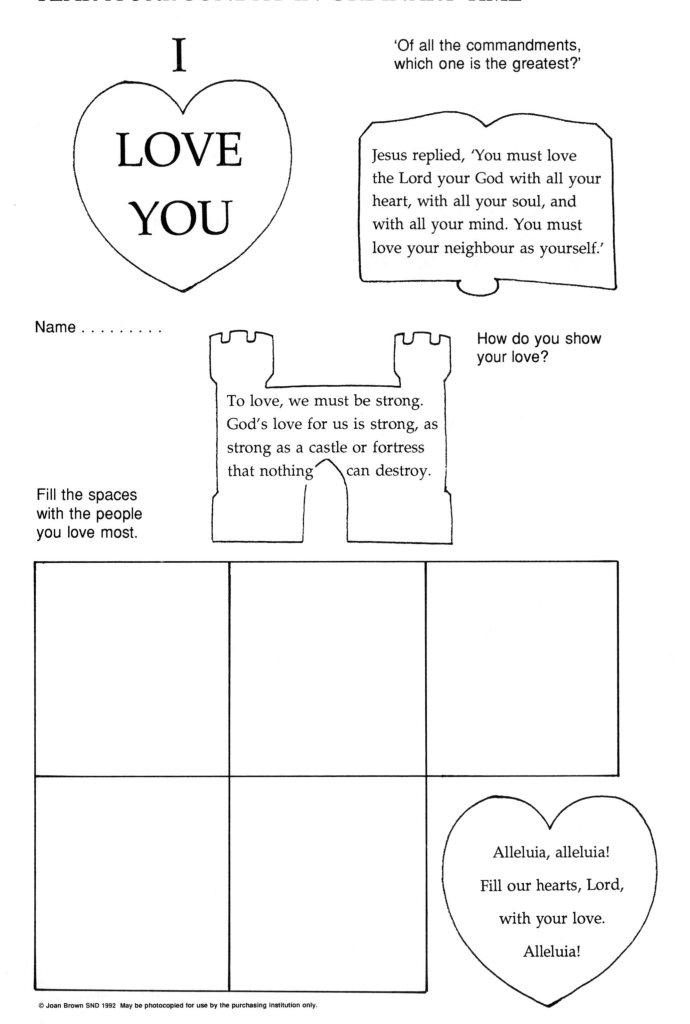

I ♥ LOVE YOU

'Of all the commandments, which one is the greatest?'

Jesus replied, 'You must love the Lord your God with all your heart, with all your soul, and with all your mind. You must love your neighbour as yourself.'

Name . . . .

How do you show your love?

To love, we must be strong. God's love for us is strong, as strong as a castle or fortress that nothing can destroy.

Fill the spaces with the people you love most.

Alleluia, alleluia!

Fill our hearts, Lord,

with your love.

Alleluia!

BE
A
GOSPEL

Everything the Scribes and Pharisees do is to attract attention to themselves and make themselves important.

You are all the one family of God our Father in heaven, so call no one on earth 'master' or 'teacher'. Rather, love and help each other.

In each tassel, write how you could do something helpful.

Then fill the tassels with bright colours. Make each one different.

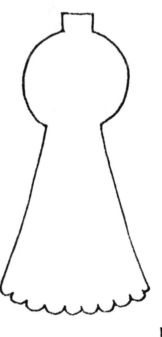

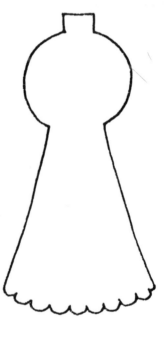

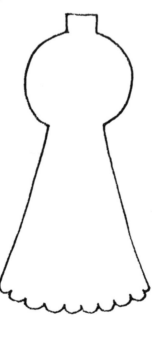

Alleluia, alleluia! The greatest amongst you must be your servant. Alleluia!

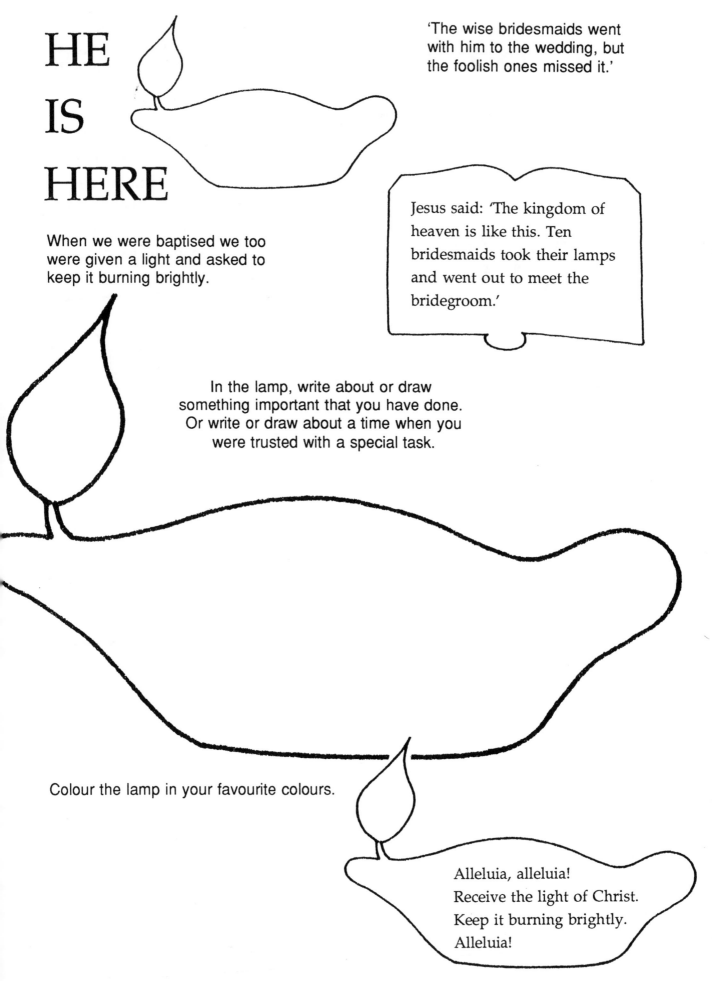

HE
IS
HERE

'The wise bridesmaids went with him to the wedding, but the foolish ones missed it.'

When we were baptised we too were given a light and asked to keep it burning brightly.

Jesus said: 'The kingdom of heaven is like this. Ten bridesmaids took their lamps and went out to meet the bridegroom.'

In the lamp, write about or draw something important that you have done. Or write or draw about a time when you were trusted with a special task.

Colour the lamp in your favourite colours.

Alleluia, alleluia!
Receive the light of Christ.
Keep it burning brightly.
Alleluia!

GLORY TO GOD

After a long time, the master returned, and called his servants to know what they had done with the talents.

'Well done, good and faithful servants. Because you can be trusted with these small things, I will trust you with greater. Come and share the happiness of my house.'

Fill the labels with your gifts from God which you most enjoy using.

Alleluia, alleluia!
Well done, good and faithful servant.
Come and join God's happiness.
Alleluia!

WELCOME

TO MY

KINGDOM

'Who are the people that my Father will welcome into the Kingdom?'

Jesus says, 'Whatever you do to the least of these my friends, you do to me.'

The whole world is Jesus' kingdom but only if we want him as our King, only if we let him rule over us, only if we let him be the King of our lives. Jesus tells us what it will be like if we let him rule our lives.

Fill the crowns with people who give you food, drink and clothing; who care for you when sick, and come to visit you.

Alleluia, alleluia!
Blessed is he who comes in the name of the Lord!
Alleluia!

WHERE DO YOU LIVE, JESUS?

John the Baptist and two of his friends were standing together when Jesus passed by.

'We want to know where

you live.'

'Come and see,' said Jesus.

Where do you live?

Write your name and address here: _ _ _ _ _ _ _ _ _ _ _ _ _ _ _ _ _ _ _

_ _ _ _ _ _ _ _ _ _ _ _ _ _ _ _ _ _ _

_ _ _ _ _ _ _ _ _ _ _ _ _ _ _ _ _ _ _

_ _ _ _ _ _ _ _ _ _ _ _ _ _ _ _ _ _ _

Draw your home.

Draw what you like most about where you live.

Whose home do you most like to visit? Draw a happy visit.

Alleluia, alleluia!
Lord, come
and make your home with us.
Alleluia!

FOLLOW ME

As he was walking by the Sea of Galilee Jesus saw two men fishing. Further along the shore, they met some more fishermen.

'Follow me', called Jesus.

Fill the boats with friends who invite you.

Draw something to which you were invited and which you enjoyed.

Alleluia, alleluia!
Lord, help us to follow you always.
Alleluia!

The people were amazed and said to each other, 'Who is this man who has such power over evil?'

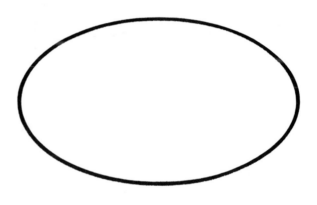

'Be quiet!' said Jesus.

'Come out of him!'

Jesus has great power. He can help us to face these difficult tasks. He has the power to change us. His power helps us love others. His power can help us to change the whole world.

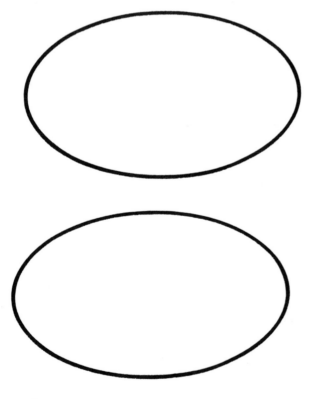

Fill the badges with hard things you can now do well.

JESUS IS LORD

Jesus,
be the Lord of our lives.
Help us spread your goodness
everywhere we go.

Alleluia, alleluia!
Jesus reveals the power of God.
Listen to his word.
Alleluia!

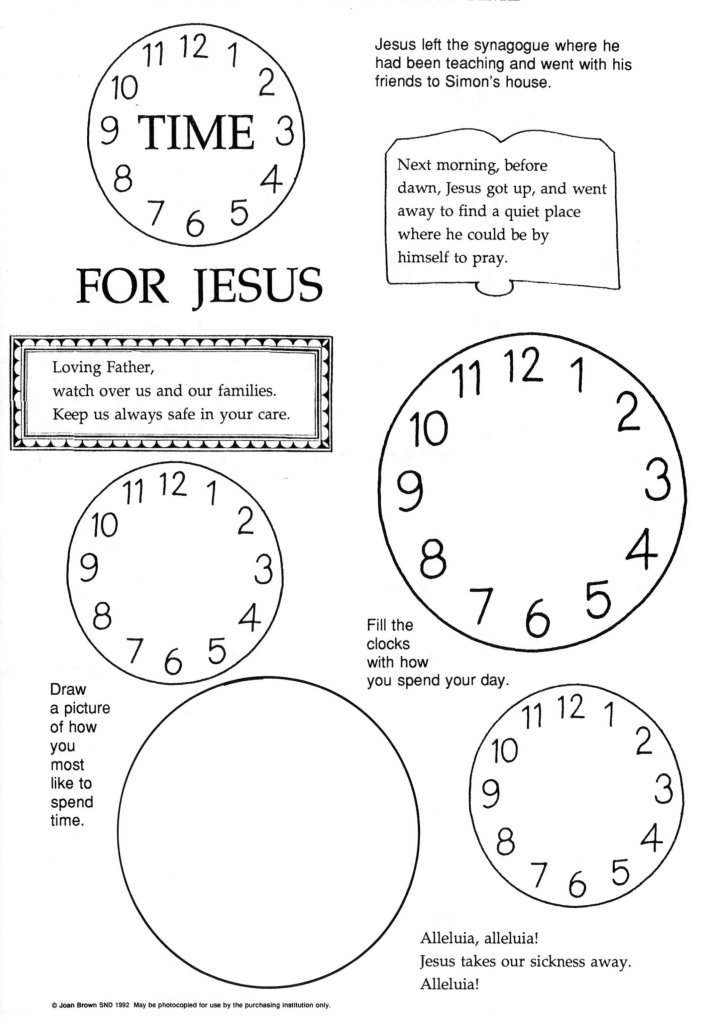

TIME

FOR JESUS

Jesus left the synagogue where he had been teaching and went with his friends to Simon's house.

Next morning, before dawn, Jesus got up, and went away to find a quiet place where he could be by himself to pray.

Loving Father,
watch over us and our families.
Keep us always safe in your care.

Fill the clocks with how you spend your day.

Draw a picture of how you most like to spend time.

Alleluia, alleluia!
Jesus takes our sickness away.
Alleluia!

The man went off and told everyone what had happened to him, spreading the news far and wide.

JESUS,

TOUCH MY HEART WITH LOVE

Jesus felt sorry for the leper, stretched out his hand and touched him. At once the man was cured.

Jesus' love in our hearts helps us to open up, to grow into being friendly people, who share what we have with others, making the world a happy place.

Fill the flowers with ways to be friendly.

Fill the hearts with the names of your friends.

Alleluia, alleluia!
Jesus saves us
and we are full of joy.
Alleluia!

FRIENDSHIP
IS ...

Jesus came back to the town of Capernaum. When the news got around, so many people came to see and listen to him that the house where he was staying was soon full to overflowing.

Four men came along, bringing their friend on a stretcher.

Lord,
give us faith
in your power to heal.
Give us friends when we are in need.
Help us to be good friends
to others when they are in need.

Seeing their faith, Jesus said to the man, 'Your sins are forgiven. Get up, pick up your bed and go home.'

Draw yourself having a good time with your friends.

Alleluia, alleluia!
Lord, increase our faith.
Alleluia!

REJOICE! JESUS IS HERE!

One day, John the Baptist, his followers and the Pharisees were fasting. Jesus and his friends were not.

Jesus said: 'Nobody would dream of fasting at a wedding while the bridegroom is still there.'

Write happy words in the hearts.

Let us pray.
Lord, help us
to make life full of joy
for those we meet this week.
Lord, hear us.
Lord, graciously hear us.
Let us pray.
Lord, fill our hearts
with the message of your Gospel.
Lord, hear us.
Lord, graciously hear us.

Draw a wedding or a happy celebration you have enjoyed.

Alleluia, alleluia!
Fill us with your love, Lord.
Alleluia!

LORD, FILL OUR HEARTS WITH LOVE

'Your friends are breaking the sabbath law by picking corn today.'

Jesus said, 'Is it against the law to do a good deed on the sabbath day?'

God has made some wonderful laws:
that we should have night and day;
that the stars stay in the sky;
that the sun shines;
that the rain falls; that plants grow;
that we can hear, see, speak . . .

Fill the shapes and
banners with
wonderful laws.

Alleluia, alleluia!
Lord, you have the message
of eternal life.
Alleluia!

© Joan Brown SND 1992 May be photocopied for use by the purchasing institution only.

YEAR B 10th SUNDAY IN ORDINARY TIME

Jesus went with his friends to Nazareth, the town where he had grown up, and where his mother still lived.

Jesus said, 'Anyone who believes in me and does the will of my Father is my brother and sister and mother.'

Jesus lived in Nazareth.

Where do you live?   I live in . . . .

. . . .

Jesus lived with Mary his mother and Joseph his foster father.

Who do you live with?...

Draw here what you like best about your family.

My family is special because it is my family.

Alleluia, alleluia!
Anyone who does God's will
is my brother and sister and mother.
Alleluia!

THE KINGDOM OF GOD IS LIKE . . .

'One day a farmer went out, planted seeds in his field, and then went home. When the farmer went back to his field, it was full of crops.'

Jesus said, 'That is what God's Kingdom is like. Even the tiniest of seeds can grow to become the biggest of trees, big enough for all the birds to make their nests in its branches.'

Fill the seeds with the ways you have grown and changed.

Fill the big seed with what you like best about the way you have grown.

Alleluia, alleluia!
May the seed of God's word grow strong in our hearts.
Alleluia!

HAVE FAITH

Jesus and his friends set sail, and other boats followed them. Suddenly a great gale began to blow, and the waves became so huge that they came into the boat, almost sinking it.

'I believe that Jesus is my friend. He will never let me down.'

'I believe God my Father loves me, and will always take care of me.'

Jesus asked his friends, 'Why were you so frightened? How is it that you didn't have faith?'

Fill the boats with people who take care of you.

Alleluia, alleluia!
Truly, Lord Jesus,
you are the Son of God.
Alleluia!

GOD

LOVES

YOU

'My little girl is very sick. Please come and lay your hands on her to make her better and save her life.'

Jesus took her by the hand and said, 'Little girl, get up.' Immediately the little girl got up and began to walk about.

Give the children happy faces.

Draw the happiest thing that ever happened to you.

Alleluia, alleluia!
Lay your hands on us
and give us life, Lord.
Alleluia!

OUR FRIEND JESUS

One sabbath day Jesus and his friends were visiting Nazareth, which is the town where Jesus had grown up. Everyone knew him and his family.

'We've known him since he was a boy. We know his mother Mary and the rest of the family.'

Draw and colour your friends. Write their names.

Draw what you enjoy doing with your friends.

Alleluia, alleluia!
Lord, increase our faith.
Alleluia!

I LIVE

Colour the children— one like you, one like your special friend.

Write in your names.

Fill the banners with good ways to live.

Jesus called together his twelve special friends, and sent them out, two by two.

Jesus said to them, 'Stay in any house where you are made welcome.'

Lord Jesus, where there is hatred let me be loving; where there is hurt let me be forgiving; where there is fighting let me bring peace; where there is sadness let me bring comfort and joy.

Draw you and your special friend having a good time together.

Alleluia, alleluia!
Lord, you have the message of eternal life.
Alleluia!

LISTEN TO MY VOICE

The friends of Jesus who went out two by two now came back, and told Jesus all that they had said and done. Jesus told them they deserved a rest and a holiday.

Draw your favourite holiday place.

They went off in

a boat to a quiet

place for some rest.

Draw a picture of what you most like to do on holiday.

Draw the place where you would most like to go for a holiday.

Alleluia, alleluia!
Lord, be our leader;
teach us your way.
Alleluia!

JESUS FEEDS THE PEOPLE

'There's a small boy here who has five barley loaves and two fishes—but that won't feed this crowd!'

Jesus said, 'Make the people sit down.' When all the people, about five thousand, were sitting on the grass, Jesus took the loaves, gave thanks, and shared them with all.

Fill the loaves and fishes with food you enjoy.

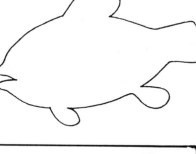

Draw yourself here enjoying a special meal.

Alleluia, alleluia!
God has visited
his people.
Alleluia!

I AM

THE BREAD OF LIFE

After Jesus had fed the five thousand people, the people wanted to make him their king.

Jesus said, 'I am the bread of life. Whoever comes to me will never be hungry again.'

Fill the bread with the gifts friends share with you.

Write your own thank-you prayer here.

Alleluia, alleluia!
We cannot live on bread alone,
but on every word
that comes from the mouth of God.
Alleluia!

JESUS IS THE LIVING BREAD

'I am the bread of life which has come down from heaven.'

Jesus said, 'The bread I shall give is myself for the life of the world.'

God gives us food for the journey, Jesus himself. Jesus gives us the strength we need for the long journey home to our Father in heaven.

Fill the shapes with journeys you have made and the food you ate on them.

I will bless the Lord always, sing his praise for ever. I will boast of his goodness to me. Good people will rejoice with me.

Glorify the Lord with me. Let us together praise his name. For God answers my prayers and cares for my every need.

Look to God for all your needs. No need to be scared. Taste, and you too will discover how good the Lord is.

Alleluia, alleluia! Jesus is the living bread who has come down from heaven. Alleluia!

REJOICE!

'The bread that I shall give is myself for the life of the world.'

JESUS IS OUR BREAD

Jesus says: 'I am the bread of life which has come down from heaven.'

God our Father,
thank you for giving us Jesus
to be our bread of life.
Help us to love you
above all things
and to reach the joy
you have prepared for us.
Help us to spread your happiness
here on earth.

It is good to be alive in such a wonderful world.

When we are alive we can work to make the world an even more beautiful and happy place.

Fill the shapes with ways to be happy.

Alleluia, alleluia!
Lord, give us the living bread
from heaven.
Alleluia!

YOU HAVE THE MESSAGE OF ETERNAL LIFE

Many of the people left Jesus and went away.

Jesus said to his twelve special friends, 'Do you want to leave me, too?' Peter answered, 'Lord, to whom shall we go? You have the message of eternal life.'

Fill the flags with happy messages.

Draw a message which made you happy.

Alleluia, alleluia!
Lord, you have the message
of eternal life.
Alleluia!

LORD, YOUR WORDS ARE LIFE

The Pharisees and the Jews in general never eat without first washing their hands. And they have many customs about scrubbing the pots and dishes too.

'If your heart is full of love,

you are clean in the eyes

of God.'

Fill the water jars with happy customs which you enjoy.

Alleluia, alleluia!
Your words, Lord, bring us life.
Alleluia!

SPEAK, LORD, WE ARE LISTENING

One day, as Jesus was travelling towards the Sea of Galilee, some people brought a man to him who was deaf and who could not speak properly.

God is faithful forever.
He gives bread to the hungry.

He protects all who call upon him.
He sets prisoners free.

God gives sight to the blind.
He opens the ears of the deaf.

He raises those who feel really down.
He protects widows and orphans.

Jesus took the man aside. Then, looking up to heaven, he said, 'Ephphatha! Be opened.' And immediately the man could hear and speak properly.

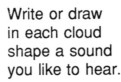

Write or draw in each cloud shape a sound you like to hear.

Alleluia, alleluia!
Jesus proclaimed the Good News, cured the people's sickness.
Alleluia!

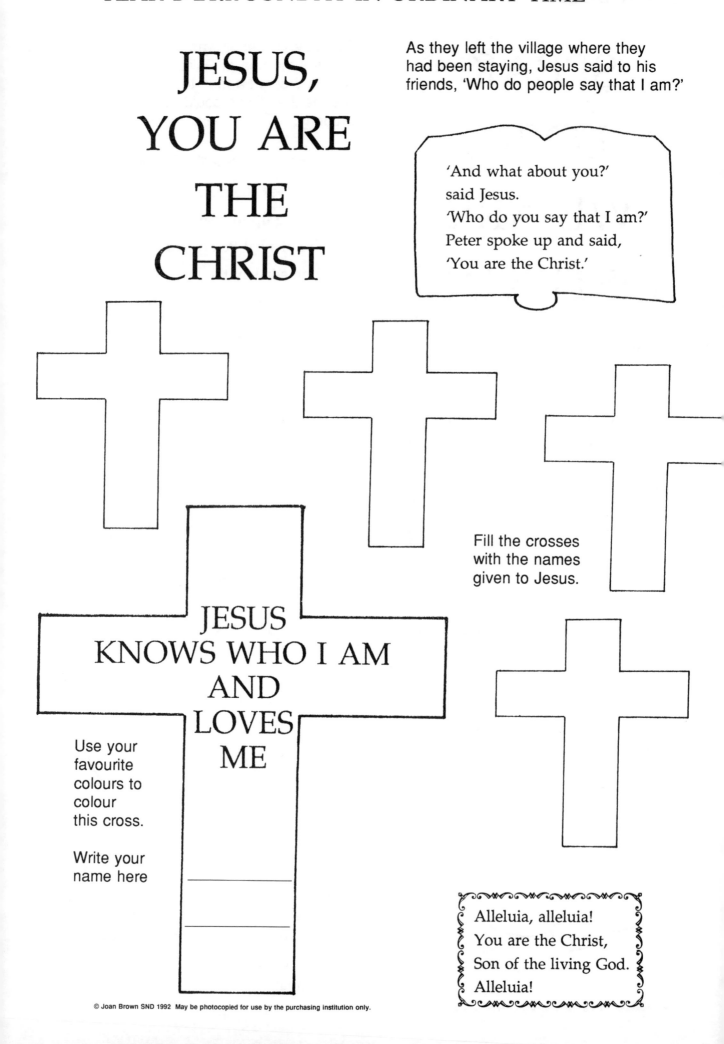

JESUS,
YOU ARE
THE
CHRIST

As they left the village where they had been staying, Jesus said to his friends, 'Who do people say that I am?'

'And what about you?'
said Jesus.
'Who do you say that I am?'
Peter spoke up and said,
'You are the Christ.'

Fill the crosses
with the names
given to Jesus.

JESUS
KNOWS WHO I AM
AND
LOVES
ME

Use your
favourite
colours to
colour
this cross.

Write your
name here

Alleluia, alleluia!
You are the Christ,
Son of the living God.
Alleluia!

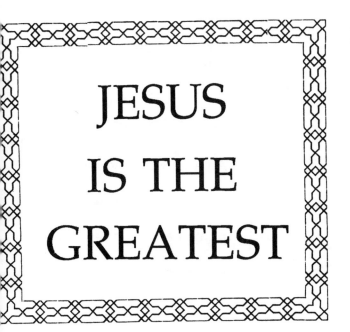

JESUS
IS THE
GREATEST

Jesus sat down, gathered his twelve friends round him and said, 'Whoever wants to be first must be last; the one who wants to be the greatest must be the servant of all.'

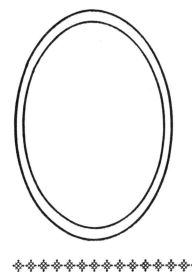

Jesus put his arms around a little child and said, 'Anyone who welcomes a little child in my name welcomes me; and when you welcome me, you welcome the one who sent me.'

Fill the badges with the most important people in your life.

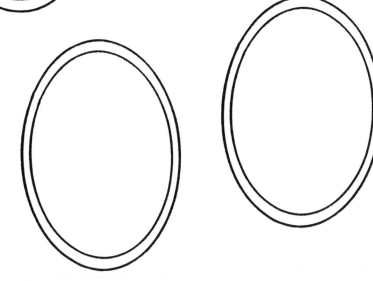

Jesus is the greatest, yet he was the servant of all. Jesus had time for everyone, even the children.

Alleluia, alleluia!
I am the light of the world.
Those who follow me
will live in light.
Alleluia!

ARE YOU FOR ME, OR AGAINST ME?

Anyone who is not against us, is for us.

Anyone who gives as little as a cup of cold water in my name will be rewarded.

God's spirit is like the wind. We cannot see the spirit, but we can see what the spirit does.
How? Where?
God's spirit is the spirit of love; the spirit shows in the lives of people who live with love.

Fill the kites with the good things done for you by your family and friends.

Love is being like Jesus, who gave everything for us, even his life.

Alleluia, alleluia!
Your word is true, Lord.
Alleluia!

WE ARE THE FAMILY OF GOD

People were bringing their children to Jesus for him to touch them.

Jesus put his arms around the children, laid his hands on them and blessed them.

Give the children happy faces.

Draw something that makes you happy.

Alleluia, alleluia!
If we live in love,
God will live in us.
Alleluia!

WE ARE RICH IN JESUS

Jesus was setting out on a journey when a young man ran up, knelt before him and asked,
'Good Master, what must I do to have eternal life?'

Jesus looked at him and loved him, and he said, 'There is one thing you have not done. Go, sell everything you own, give the money to the poor, and you will have treasure in heaven. Then come, follow me.'

Fill the shapes with what Jesus loves about you.

Alleluia, alleluia!
Happy are the poor in spirit;
theirs is the Kingdom of heaven.
Alleluia!

JESUS
SETS US
FREE
TO LOVE

James and John came to Jesus and said, 'Master, we want to ask you a favour.' 'What is it?' Jesus asked. 'Allow us to sit with you in glory.'

Fill the invitations with friends who have done favours for you.

Jesus said, 'Real greatness comes from serving others. This is what I came to do, to serve others, and to give my life to set them free.'

Alleluia, alleluia!
Jesus came to serve,
to give his life for us.
Alleluia!

JESUS, THE LIGHT WITHIN US

'Master, let me see again.'

'Go,' said Jesus, 'your faith has saved you.'

Fill the lights with what you are happy to see.

Alleluia, alleluia!
Jesus is the light of the world.
Let us follow him.
Alleluia!

BIND US TOGETHER IN LOVE

'Which is the first of the commandments?'

Jesus replied, 'This is the first: to love the Lord your God with all your heart and with all your strength. The second is this: to love everybody as you love yourself.'

A loving person is a strong person. God's love is the strongest love of all.

Fill the castles with all the people who love you.

Here write a prayer asking God to help you to be strong in love.

Alleluia, alleluia!
The Lord is our strength
and our help.
Alleluia!

TRUST JESUS

Along came a poor widow. She put two small coins in the box. They were the smallest of all coins, worth less than a penny.

Do we thank God enough for giving us everything, but especially for giving us Jesus?

Jesus saw what she put in and said to his friends: 'This poor woman has put more into the box than anyone else. Others gave from what they had to spare; but she put in everything she had, all she had to live on.'

Fill the boxes with gifts — coins of love you can give to others.

In this box write a prayer to thank God for giving us Jesus.

Alleluia, alleluia!
Happy are the poor in spirit,
for theirs is the kingdom of heaven.
Alleluia!

JESUS

IS

NEAR

Do not be afraid.

Jesus said to his friends, 'I will come and gather all my friends together from every corner of the earth.'

Jesus wants us to be happy with him in his kingdom of love.

Fill the houses with happy scenes. Then use your colours to make this a happy picture.

Alleluia, alleluia!
Jesus is with us always.
Alleluia!

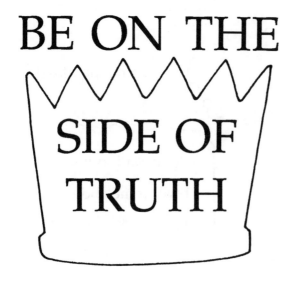

'Are you the King of the Jews?'

Jesus says, 'I came into the world to speak up for the truth.'

Use your colours to decorate the crowns for Jesus.
Or
fill them with TRUTH about Jesus.

Alleluia, alleluia!
Blessed is the one who comes in the name of the Lord.
Alleluia!

YEAR C 2nd SUNDAY IN ORDINARY TIME

'This is wonderful wine. Why didn't you serve this wine to your guests first?'

BELIEVE!

Mary said to the servants,

'Do whatever Jesus tells

you to do.'

For you who believe, the whole world is full of God's glory. For you who believe, the little drops of water of everyday life are changed, when you are loving and kind as Jesus asks us to be.

Fill the jars with what you do every day.

Alleluia, alleluia!
Jesus let his glory be seen
so that we may believe in him.
Alleluia!

YEAR C 3rd SUNDAY IN ORDINARY TIME

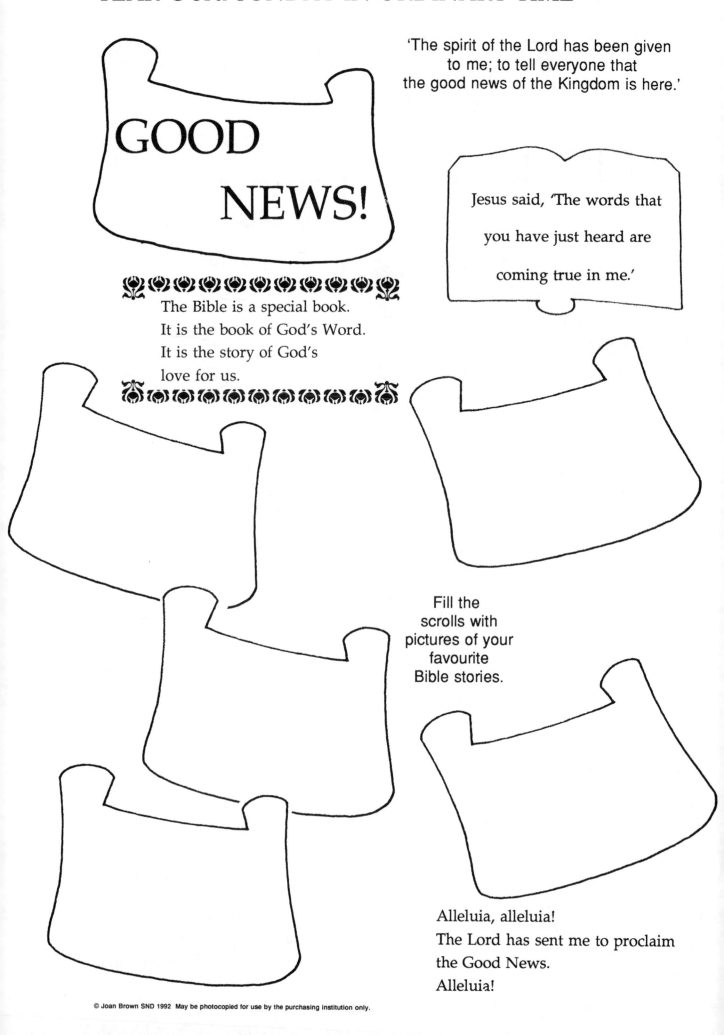

'The spirit of the Lord has been given to me; to tell everyone that the good news of the Kingdom is here.'

GOOD NEWS!

The Bible is a special book. It is the book of God's Word. It is the story of God's love for us.

Jesus said, 'The words that you have just heard are coming true in me.'

Fill the scrolls with pictures of your favourite Bible stories.

Alleluia, alleluia! The Lord has sent me to proclaim the Good News. Alleluia!

BE TRUE

The people were amazed, because he made the scriptures so clear by the way he read and explained them.

Jesus said, 'The Kingdom of God is here. You must change your ways.'

We are all different.
We look different.
We feel different.
We think differently.
We walk differently.
We talk differently.
But we try to love each and every one as they are.
We do not pretend to be what we are not.
We try to be true to ourselves.

Fill the hearts with what is true about yourself.

Alleluia, alleluia!
The Lord has sent me
to proclaim the Good News.
Alleluia!

FOLLOW ME

Simon and the other fishermen threw the nets into the lake, and caught so many fish that the nets began to tear and the weight nearly made the boats sink. Simon and the other fishermen, James and John, were amazed.

Jesus said, 'Don't be afraid: from now on you will be fishers of men.'

Fill the fish with times when you have been very surprised.

Alleluia, alleluia!
Follow me, says the Lord,
and I will make you fishers of men.
Alleluia!

HAPPINESS BRINGS PEACE

Jesus climbed up a little hill where he sat down. His friends went with him and a crowd of people followed them. Jesus sat down and began to speak to them: 'Happiness is putting God first.'

'Happiness is rejoicing that your reward is very great in heaven.'

In the flowers draw:
Happy Kindness
Happy Giving
Happy Sharing

HAPPINESS IS GROWING IN GOD'S LOVE

Alleluia, alleluia!
Happy are those who hear
the Word of God
and keep it.
Alleluia!

SHARE WHAT YOU HAVE

Whatever you give one another,
God will always give you more.

Jesus says to his friends,
'You must be like your
Father in heaven.'

Jesus tells us how we can be
more like God our Father who is
so generous to us all.

Fill the boxes
with what other
people and family
and friends share
with you, and what
you can share with them.

Alleluia, alleluia!
Love one another
as God loves everyone.
Alleluia!

LOOK

AND

SEE

Why is it that people are too quick to pick out faults in those around them?

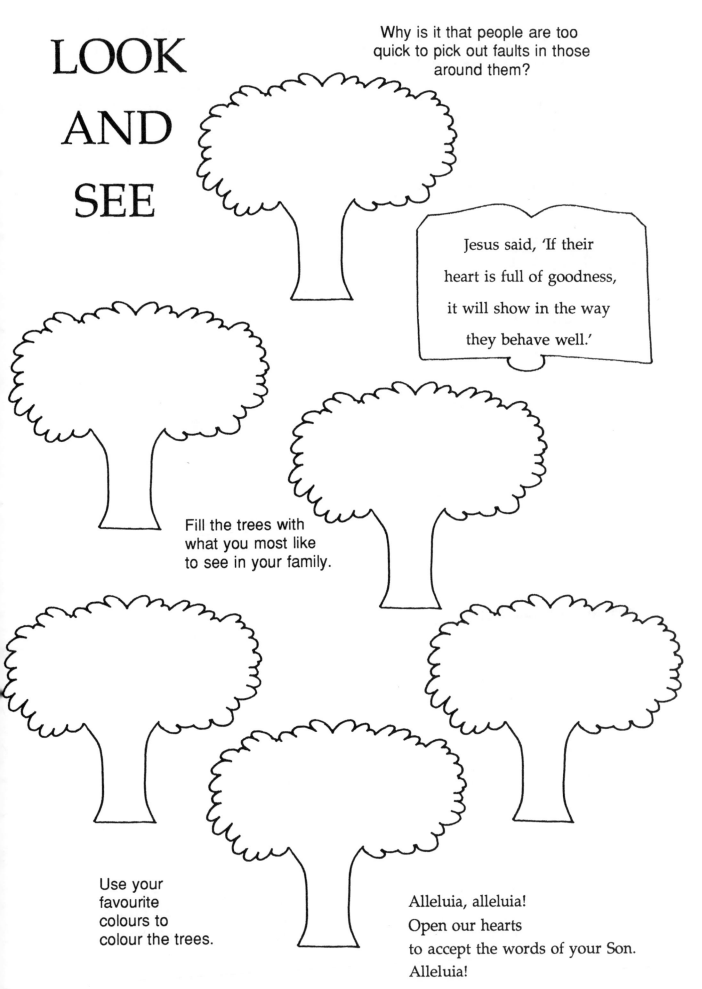

Jesus said, 'If their heart is full of goodness, it will show in the way they behave well.'

Fill the trees with what you most like to see in your family.

Use your favourite colours to colour the trees.

Alleluia, alleluia!
Open our hearts
to accept the words of your Son.
Alleluia!

FRIENDSHIP IS BRINGING JESUS TO EACH OTHER

'Sir, don't put yourself to the trouble of coming to the house. Just as I can order my soldiers, so you can order the illness to leave my servant. I am not worthy to have you under my roof.'

Jesus said, 'This man, a pagan, has shown more faith than any of God's chosen people.'

Our best friend is Jesus.

Write the names of your friends in the posters.

Draw how your friends help to make you happy.

Alleluia, alleluia!
God loved the world so much
he gave his only Son.
Alleluia!

THANK YOU FOR THE GIFT OF NEW LIFE

Just as Jesus and his friends were coming into a town called Nain, they met a funeral carrying out a dead man to be buried.

Jesus said, 'Young man, I tell you, get up!' The dead man sat up and began to talk.

On Sunday we come to Mass to praise God for the new life we have received.

People I know at Mass

On the candle, write your name and the date of your baptism — your New Life Day. Colour the candle.

Names of New Life people I know

My own thank-you prayer for New Life

My favourite Mass prayer

Alleluia, alleluia!
God has visited his people.
Alleluia!

GO IN PEACE

'She has shown great love because her many sins have been forgiven.'

We are anointed in baptism and confirmation. This anointing is a sign of having become God's children. God's anointing is a sign of his great love for us.

Turning to the woman, Jesus said, 'Go in peace, your faith has saved you.'

Fill the perfume-oil bottles with times when you have been forgiven. Show the people who have forgiven you.

'Jesus forgives you. Go in peace.'

Write your own 'sorry' prayer here.

Alleluia, alleluia!
God loved us so much he sent his only Son
to take our sins away.
Alleluia!

FOLLOW ME

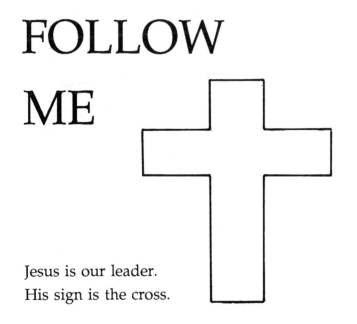

One day, after he had been praying, Jesus said to his friends, 'If you want to follow me, you will not find it easy.'

'I am ready to suffer and die for you. Anyone who follows me must be ready to do the same.'

Jesus is our leader.
His sign is the cross.

Once upon a time there were two great leaders: one was very bad and one was good and kind. From time to time these leaders called their followers to speak to them.

How would the bad leader speak?

Softly and kindly . . .?

Would he yell and shout . . .?

Draw the bad leader and his followers.

How would the good leader speak?

Would he be kind and firm?

Would he bawl and shout?

Draw the good leader and his followers.

Alleluia, alleluia!
Anyone who follows me
will have the light of life.
Alleluia!

YEAR C 13th SUNDAY IN ORDINARY TIME

'I'll follow you wherever you go.'

FOLLOW ME

Jesus said, 'You must make up your mind what you want to do, and then do that. Anyone who looks back after setting out with me is not fit for the Kingdom of heaven.'

How does Jesus call us to follow him today?

In the flags, draw how you can show that you follow Jesus
at home . . .
at school . . .
at play . . .

Alleluia, alleluia!
Lord, show us the path of life.
Alleluia!

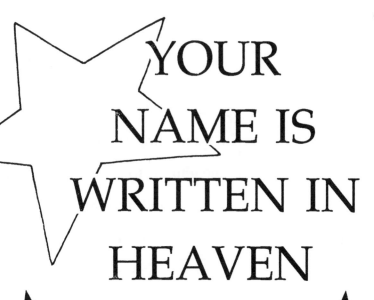

YOUR NAME IS WRITTEN IN HEAVEN

One day Jesus chose seventy-two people to help him with his work of spreading the Good News.

Jesus said, 'Rejoice that your names are written in heaven.'

It is wonderful to use your life to benefit others.

Fill the stars with people and groups who work to help others.

Alleluia, alleluia!
Rejoice, because
your names are written in heaven.
Alleluia!

MY NEIGHBOUR IS . . .

A Samaritan felt sorry for the injured man, so he went over to him, cleaned up his cuts and bandaged them.

Jesus asks us to open our hearts to help others in whatever way we can.

Jesus said, 'Who was the neighbour to the man who fell into the hands of the bandits?'

In the hearts, draw some people who need help today.

How can you help them?

Alleluia, alleluia!
Those who belong to me
listen to my voice.
I know them and they love me.
Alleluia!

ONLY ONE THING IS IMPORTANT

Jesus came to a village and went to visit his friends Martha and Mary. Martha welcomed him.

Jesus said, 'Martha, Martha! You worry too much. Mary chose the right thing for her. You should do what you have chosen to do.'

It is important that each one of us should do whatever we can for Jesus.

Fill the clocks with how you share time with others.

Alleluia, alleluia! Happy are those with a generous heart. Alleluia!

LORD, TEACH US TO PRAY

One day, when Jesus had finished praying, his friends asked him, 'Lord, teach us to pray.'

Our world is a very beautiful place.

It is God's gift to us.

This is what Jesus taught them: 'Say this when you pray. Our Father, who art in heaven, hallowed be thy name.'

Let us pray that the beauty of the world we see around us will open our eyes to the wonder of God and his love for us.

Father in heaven, we thank you for all your goodness to us. Fill our hearts with your love. Help us always to share ourselves and what we have with each other.

Alleluia, alleluia! It is the spirit you have received that makes you pray 'Father'. Alleluia!

Use your favourite colours to make this prayer poster.

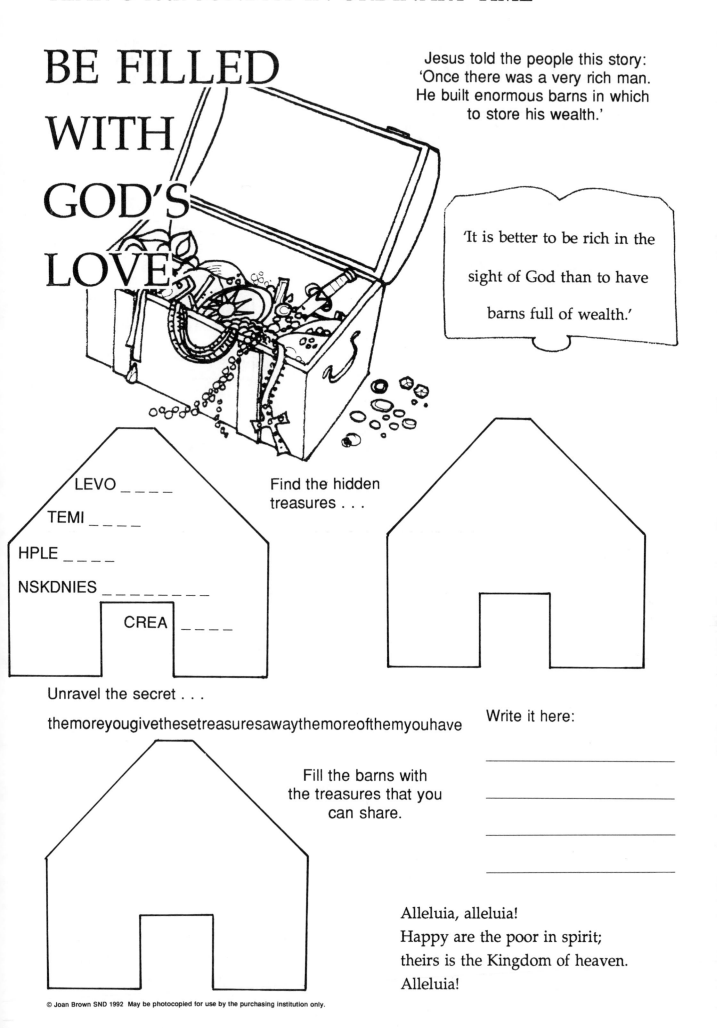

BE FILLED WITH GOD'S LOVE

Jesus told the people this story:
'Once there was a very rich man.
He built enormous barns in which
to store his wealth.'

'It is better to be rich in the
sight of God than to have
barns full of wealth.'

Find the hidden
treasures . . .

LEVO _ _ _ _

TEMI _ _ _ _

HPLE _ _ _ _

NSKDNIES _ _ _ _ _ _ _ _

CREA _ _ _ _

Unravel the secret . . .

themoreyougivethesetreasuresawaythemoreofthemyouhave

Write it here:

_____

_____

Fill the barns with
the treasures that you
can share.

_____

_____

Alleluia, alleluia!
Happy are the poor in spirit;
theirs is the Kingdom of heaven.
Alleluia!

YOUR HEART IS WHERE YOUR TREASURE IS

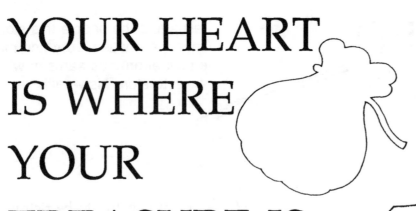

'Your heart is where
your treasure is,
so make sure your treasure
is in heaven.'

Jesus says:

'God will give you treasure
in heaven which no one can
steal or destroy.'

Fill the purses
with treasure
which cannot be stolen
or spoilt.

Alleluia, alleluia!
Happy are the poor in spirit;
theirs is the Kingdom of heaven.
Alleluia!

I HAVE COME TO BRING FIRE

Jesus said to his friends,
'I have come to bring fire
to the earth.'

Jesus says:
'People must make up their
minds whether or not they
are going to follow me.'

Praise to you, Lord,
for our brother fire.
He is handsome, joyous and strong.
Thanks to him, we are kept warm.
Thanks to him, we have light at night.

Colour the
border with
fiery colours.

Fill the flames
with more
good things
about fire.

Alleluia, alleluia!
Open our hearts, Lord, and
fill them with the fire of your love.
Alleluia!

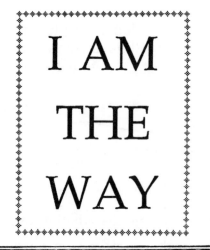

I AM THE WAY

In one village someone asked,
'Sir, will many be saved, or only a few?'

Jesus replied, 'The door to the
Kingdom of heaven is narrow,
but you must try to get
through.'

— by being like Jesus we find our way through to the Father.

Fill the
doorways
with
journeys
you have
made
and
how
you
found
your
way.
Or show
your
favourite
journey.

Or how you
find
your
way
home,
to school,
or
to church.

Alleluia, alleluia!
I am the way, says the Lord.
Through me you find the Father.
Alleluia!

FRIEND, COME CLOSER TO ME

One day one of the leading Pharisees invited Jesus to his house for a meal.

Jesus said, 'When you give a meal, don't invite only those you know will invite you back in return.'

Fill the chalices with people you can help . . . or times when you can let others go first . . . or let others choose.

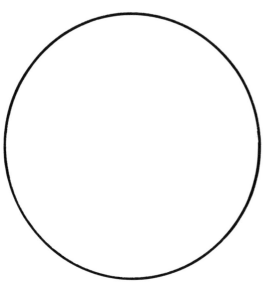

Alleluia, alleluia!
Learn from me, says the Lord.
Alleluia!

BE MY FRIENDS

Jesus turned to the great crowd that was following him and said, 'Following me is not easy. You must know what it will involve.'

God made us and loves us. He never gets bored with loving and looking after us.

'If you want to follow me, you must know what it will mean. You must be prepared to follow me all the way to the end.'

Fill the spaces with things you have made or done that were difficult.

Alleluia, alleluia!
Lord, teach us to do
what you want us to do.
Alleluia!

LET
HEAVEN
REJOICE

'Imagine you were a shepherd with a flock of 100 sheep, and you lost one. Wouldn't you go out to look for the one lost sheep?'

Jesus said, 'God your Father welcomes back anyone who is lost.'

MY LOST
SHEEP
IS FOUND.

REJOICE!
REJOICE!
HURRAY!

Fill the sheep with times you or anyone in your family has been lost and found or has lost and found something.

Alleluia, alleluia!
May God help us see and find the treasure he has for us.
Alleluia!

BE A WISE SERVANT

You must never be the slave of money.

Then Jesus said to his friends, 'You must learn to use things wisely to gain your home in heaven.'

Just as the servant used the things of this world to make sure he had a home, so we must learn to use the things of this world wisely and properly to reach our heavenly home.

Be wise . . .
Share
what
you
have.

Fill the tags with what is shared with you at home, at school and at play.

Alleluia, alleluia!
Jesus was rich,
but became poor for your sake,
so that he could make you rich.
Alleluia!

LORD, FILL OUR HEARTS WITH LOVE

Once there was a rich man, who dressed beautifully and lived expensively, only eating the very best. At the gate of his house lay a beggar called Lazarus.

One day the poor man died

and the angels carried him to

heaven.

Father, thank you
for all the love and kindness
you have shown towards us.
Help us to be loving and kind
towards others in return.
Father, thank you
for the food we have.
Help us not to be greedy and
wasteful with it.
Help us to share with those who
do not have enough food.

Fill the plates with ways to help children in need.

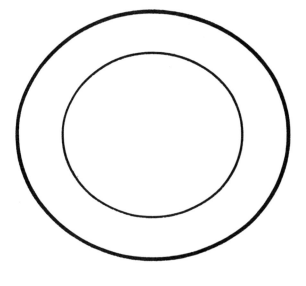

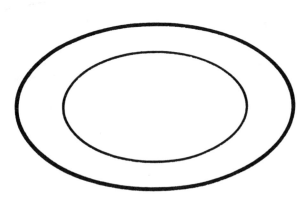

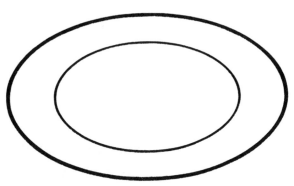

How can you help?

Alleluia, alleluia!
Jesus was rich,
but became poor for your sake,
so that he could make you rich.
Alleluia!

LORD, INCREASE OUR FAITH

One day Jesus' friends said to him, 'Lord, make our faith bigger.'

Write your own prayer of faith in the tree.

I believe God made me.
I believe Jesus died and rose to save me.
I believe the Spirit gives me life.

Jesus replied, 'The size of your faith doesn't matter.'

Fill the seeds with all that you might grow into.

Alleluia, alleluia!
Lord, increase our faith.
Alleluia!

LET US GIVE THANKS TO THE LORD

As Jesus travelled towards Jerusalem, near one of the villages, ten lepers came out to meet him.

Fill the space with what you are most thankful for.

Jesus said, 'Stand up and go on your way. Your faith has saved you.'

Draw a time when you were sick.

Draw the people who looked after you.

Draw when you recovered.

Write your own 'Thank-you' prayer for good health.

Alleluia, alleluia!
For all things give thanks,
because that is what God expects
you to do in Christ Jesus.
Alleluia!

NEVER LOSE HEART

Even the unjust judge gave the woman what she wanted when she kept asking; how much more will God your Father do for you when you ask him.

Jesus told his friends,

'When you pray, you must

never lose heart.'

Fill this heart with the hardest thing you ever did.

What does it feel like not to succeed? And if we don't succeed the first time, what should we do? Try again . . .

Fill the hearts with some things that you will put all your heart into doing this week.

You can write or draw.

Alleluia, alleluia!
God's word is active and alive.
Alleluia!

HAVE MERCY ON ME, JESUS

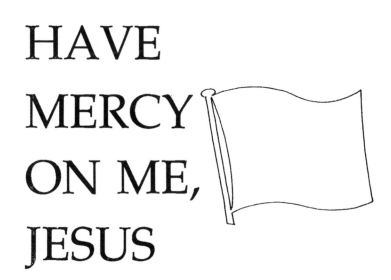

'The Pharisee began his prayer like this: "Lord, I thank you that I am not like the rest of men, not like this greedy tax collector. Thank you, God. I do everything I should do and much more." The tax collector stood at the back and didn't even lift his eyes to heaven. He prayed, "God, have mercy on me, a sinner."'

We rejoice at the victory of God.
We make our boast in his great name.
We boast of his goodness.
We boast of his love.
We boast of his justice and mercy.

Jesus asked:

'Whose prayer do you think God listened to?'

Fill the flags with good things you have done to help others.

Write your own mercy prayer for when you have refused to help.

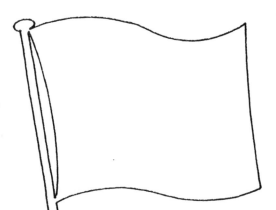

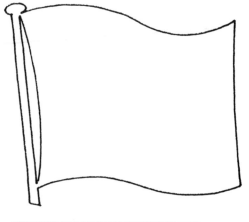

Alleluia, alleluia!
God, through Jesus, grants mercy to all.
Alleluia!

TODAY I MUST STAY AT YOUR HOUSE

'Zacchaeus', Jesus said, 'come down. Hurry because today I must stay at your house.'

'Today, salvation has come to this house.'

Jesus calls to us

— to listen to him

— to welcome him

— to change our lives for Jesus.

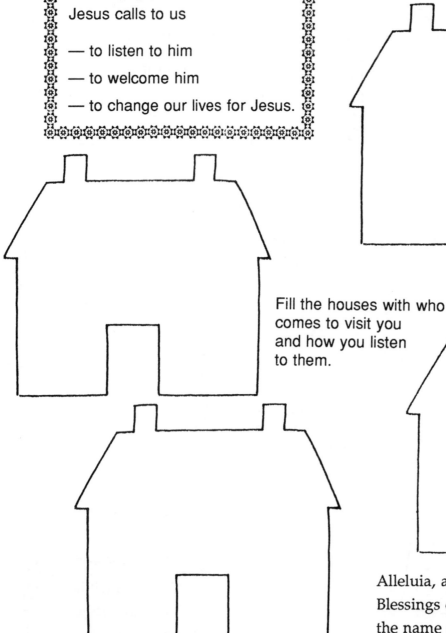

Fill the houses with who comes to visit you and how you listen to them.

Alleluia, alleluia!
Blessings on the one who comes in the name of the Lord.
Alleluia!

WE WILL RISE AGAIN

'At the resurrection whose wife will she be?'

Jesus replied, 'There will be no need for marriage for those who rise to new life, for they will be the same as the angels and children of God.'

The promise of new life is in the seeds.

Write or draw in the seeds any promises which have come true for you.

Colour the flowers.

Alleluia, alleluia!
Jesus is the first-born from the dead;
to him be glory for ever.
Alleluia!

YEAR C 33rd SUNDAY IN ORDINARY TIME

NOT A HAIR OF YOUR HEAD WILL BE LOST

One day when Jesus was in the Temple, some people were admiring its stonework and ornate carvings. They were full of praise for it.

Jesus said, 'You are more precious than any building, even this one.'

People are more wonderful than any building on earth.
People can make buildings but it is God who makes people.
Each person is a home for God on earth.

Fill the children with the ways you are looked after and cared for.

Jesus tells us never to be afraid. No matter what happens, God will always be there to look after us.

Alleluia, alleluia!
Lord, come and make your home in us.
Alleluia!

YOU WILL BE WITH ME IN PARADISE

'Jesus, remember me, when you come into your Kingdom.'

Jesus replied,
'I promise you,
this day
you will be
with me
in paradise.'

Jesus has chosen to share his power with all who are baptised. He wants us to use this power in the same way that he did: to help others and to bring them home to paradise.

Jesus is the King of all creation. Because Jesus defeated evil and death on the cross, God has made him King of everything that is living, of everything that is.

Colour the picture of creation.

Alleluia, alleluia!
Blessed is the one
who comes in the name of the Lord.
Alleluia!